PetMassage E

MW00667678

Jill Hayden
352-322-8348

PetMassage Energy Work with Dogs

# PetMassage™ Energy Work with Dogs

## Accessing the Magnificent Body Language & Body Wisdom of the Dog

# Also by Jonathan Rudinger

PetMassage$_{TM}$: Art and Essence of Canine Massage

Effective Pet Massage for Dogs, Manual

Effective Pet Massage for Dogs, *DVD*

Effective Pet Massage for Older Dogs, *DVD*

Transitions, PetMassage$_{TM}$ Energy Work for the Aging and Dying Dog

PetMassage$_{TM}$: Energy Work With Dogs, Accessing the Magnificent Body Language & Body Wisdom of the Dog , *5 Audio CD Set*

PetMassage$_{TM}$: A Kid's Guide to Massaging Dogs, *DVD*

PetMassage$_{TM}$: Doggie Songs for Kids, *Audio CD*

Dogs Kids PetMassage

Creating & Marketing Your Animal Massage Business

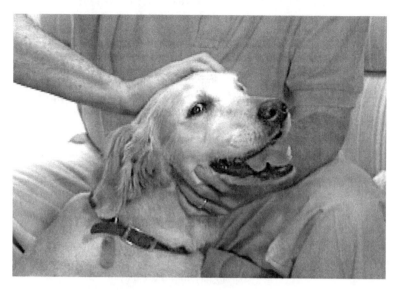

# PetMassage™ Energy Work with Dogs

*Accessing the Magnificent Body Language & Body Wisdom of the Dog*

## Jonathan Rudinger, RN, LMT
Founder of the PetMassage™ Institute

ENERGY WORK WITH DOGS, *Accessing the Magnificent Body Language & Body Wisdom of the Dog*

*For information address* PetMassageᴛᴍ books, PetMassageᴛᴍ, Ltd. 3347 McGregor Lane, Toledo, OH 43623 USA.

PetMassageᴛᴍ and its logo, the image of a person massaging a dog, on a rectangular background, are the trademarks of PetMassageᴛᴍ books, PetMassageᴛᴍ, Ltd. 3347 McGregor Lane, Toledo, OH 43623 USA

Visit our website at www.PetMassage.com

Rudinger, Jonathan C.

Energy Work with Dogs, Accessing the Magnificent Body Language and Body Wisdom of the Dog
*Jonathan Rudinger – Revised Edition.*

*Includes bibliographical references.*
1. *Pet Care* 2. *Holistic Animal Care* 3. *Massage Dog Massage* 4. *Alternative Veterinary medicine* 5. *Acupressure Animal* 6. *Communication Dogs—Social Aspects—Anecdotes* 7. *Dogs—Therapeutic uses—Anecdotes* 8. *Human Animal Relationships*
9. *PetMassageᴛᴍ Training & Research Institute*

Photographs on pages vi, xi, 13, 22 38, 39, 44, 95, 122, 132, 152, 303 and front and back covers are the work of Cheryl Hall, Cheryl Hall, Photography.

 PetMassage Books

ISBN 0-9664826-3-8 Third Edition

## Dedication

*This is for all the horses, dogs, cats and other critters and their caring people that I have had the honor to connect with since I started working with animals in the early 1980's. Thank you for trusting me, so that I could allow my intuitive nature to lead me to develop the methods in this course.*

*I thank you, Anastasia, my wife and guide, for maintaining your sense of humor with an obsessive writer and dreamer. Thank you to my assistants, Barb Harris and Beth Farkas. Your help and support have been essential. And a big ol' hug to my daughter, Samantha, and her growing family, for reminding me that I had told her over two years ago, before the last 6 drafts of this book, that it was almost done. Thank you all for your patience and encouragement.*
*-JR*

Massage is not, nor is it intended to be a substitute for traditional veterinary care. It is a complementary form of health care. The information is provided for the purposes of education and to give as complete a description as possible. The reader should regularly consult a veterinarian in matters relating to his or her dog's health and especially in regard to any symptoms, which may require diagnosis or medical attention. If you have any questions regarding the efficacy of any of the techniques suggested in this manual, please consult with your veterinarian or qualified animal massage practitioner.

Working with any animal involves inherent risk. While general massage techniques are all to be applied lovingly and gently, any receiver, animal or human, will react negatively to strokes that may feel abusive, invasive, or inappropriate. The author and agents of Energy Work for Dogs, assume no risk for injury incurred while learning to massage your dog.

Return to innocence.

Push with your heart, not with your hands.

PetMassage is a harmonious connection with your pet.

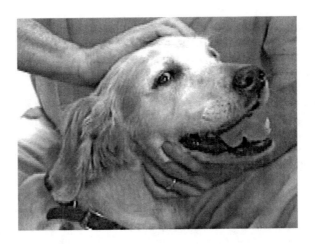

PetMassage Energy Work with Dogs

## Contents

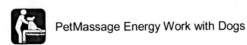 PetMassage Energy Work with Dogs

**List of Exercises**

Introduction

Thank you for your interest and enthusiasm in learning PetMassage<sub>TM</sub>. I am your instructor for this course in PetMassage<sub>TM</sub> Energy Work for dogs.

We begin each of our workshops by getting to know each other; with sharing our stories about the paths we took that got us to this place and time.

My story is probably pretty similar to yours. My family had dogs and cats as I was growing up.

*Jonathan with Oskar, the Boxer*

The animals and I communicated with each other very naturally. I recall bringing Pepper, one of our dogs, into a supermarket. It never occurred to me to ask permission as we, Pepper and I walked to the dog food aisle in the back of the store. I'd line up the different cans of food on the floor and ask him which one he'd prefer. His favorite was always the one with the German Shepherd on the label; it was the one he'd tip over with his *nose*.

As an adult, I learned that this ability to understand and be understood by animals is not universal. It is unusual and precious.

The information in this course was taught to me mostly by dogs, cats and horses. The rest I learned by adapting human medical massage theory, fundamentals of martial arts, Healing Touch, aspects of esoteric forms of positional release and myofascia work and intuitively developed techniques.

A word about intuitive development: I have not invented anything, here. Animal massage has been around as long as people have interacted with animals. All of the thoughts and experiences of people and animals are included in the huge pool of human/animal cultural memory called the Akashic Record. The Akasha is the record of all life's thoughts and feelings. It is, for want of a better term, the spiritual database, that clairvoyants such as Edgar Casey access while in their trance-state. It is real. It is accessible. It is outside time and space. And, it is as much a part of each of our genetic memories as eye color or our talents.

Sometimes, while going about our daily lives, we are fortunate to be able to recall some piece of information, a memory that we'd not previously realized. When it happens to me, I get a giddy feeling of being oh-so wise! I think, "I've invented (or thought of) something entirely new. *No* one's ever thought of this before." Then I figure out that I've just become aware of a tiny speck in this tremendous pool of wisdom and information. I've somehow, unwittingly tapped into this huge reservoir of human and animal memory. It's there all the time. I'm just too busy (or unaware) to notice it. One glimpse into this record is an insight. Several glimpses taken together can develop into a system.

I have been blessed with some life experiences that have enabled me to occasionally be aware when I was presented with these delightful lessons. It was with one of these epiphanies that the PetMassage$_{TM}$ form was created. Here's my story:

Working with horses, I had been developing my techniques since the early 1980's. In 1997, I was invited to give a demonstration of equine massage for a television station. As the shoot was ending, my interviewer brought an old yellow farm dog over to me, saying to the camera, "Dogs get stiff necks, too. Let's see what Jonathan can do." I thought to myself, "Oh my, this is kind of a challenge."

I cradled the dog's head in my hands and watched in delight as his tongue loll out of one side of his mouth. As his head lolled back into my hands in bliss, I experienced an immediate, profound and extraordinary insight. An epiphany! I had the knowledge and the experience to produce courses that would enable pet owners, pet-care professionals and other massage therapists to connect with and help their dogs using my PetMassage$_{TM}$ form. I saw the dogs, the students, the schools, the research, the covers of the books and videos and much, much more. This fraction of a second insight was so powerful that it moved me in ways that I had never known before. It is motivating me still, more than 5 years later.

Following the plan that I witnessed in that split second, in the years since then, we have created the videos, books, home study courses and a research institute. We have gained local as well as international recognition and draw students from all over the globe to our workshops.

My learning curve grows ever steeper. Each day brings more insights, more challenges, and more awareness of the immensity of the vision. I am growing and evolving. The workshops I taught just two years ago have evolved from the fundamentals of the first book and videos to include much of what is in this book. I see the future to be a continuation of the present. PetMassage$_{TM}$ as a profession is growing and evolving. Those whom we train are also becoming more recognized, accepted and valued. This is my path.

Everything that we have experienced: all our travels, our relationships, our jobs, our loves, successes and disappointments, each and every one of all the people and animals we've met, have directed us to this time and place.

Please take a few minutes to review your own life. What were the paths and choices you made that led you to this moment. Think about the people and pets that most influenced you along the way. Silently thank them and smile.

I thank you again for joining me as we learn more about the effects of PetMassage$_{TM}$ and the amazing workings of energy.

You are now ready to learn PetMassage$_{TM}$ Energy Work for Dogs.

This course will help you to enhance the energetic quality of your life and the lives of your animals. Dogs are energetic creatures in many ways. Those of us, who have survived Beagle or Lab puppies, know more about puppy energy than most of us ever need to know! The constant movement, the curiosity, the nonstop play are indicators of high animation; kinetic energy. The magnificent stillness we experience as the puppies collapse into sleep creates potential energy.

*Oskar and Jocko playing*

As I watch our two dogs while writing this, I see identifiable qualities to their energy. Our 3-month-old Standard Poodle is vital and ephemeral, while our 6-year-old boxer is more settled and solid. Each of their energies is unique. The qualities of energies each exudes are not static; they fluctuate with their thoughts and moods. Nor are they confined to within their bodies.

In 1997, when I completed the first video, "Effective Pet Massage for Dogs, Volume 1," my wife, Anastasia and I would travel to promote the course at shopping malls, bookstores, dog shows and animal adoption events. When I'd tell people what I do, they'd often laugh. The response was often "Massage my dog? Why would I ever want to massage my dog?"

*Agility dogs athletes*

I would tell them just a few of the many benefits: that it helps older dogs that are stiff with arthritis regain ease of movement and flexibility; and that it can be used to help modify unpleasant doggie behavior. It is being used as part of post-surgery veterinary rehabilitation programs. It's a great way to bond with dogs and, it's a terrific way for dog owners to maintain a consistent assessment of their dog's health.

After a little reflection, our nay-sayers usually smiled and said, "What a great idea! It does make sense, a lot of sense. How long has this been around?" And, "Why haven't I heard of this before?" Agility trainers recognize the obvious fact that their dogs are athletes and need to be treated as such. Their dogs often get massage therapy when their muscles get sore, or when they need to warm up or cool down at competitions.

*Show dogs need massage, too.*

Top handlers of show dogs know that massage helps their dogs win.

We see the profound relationships people have with their pets.

| PetMassage helps dogs win. |
| :---: |

As our families become more fragmented, and single people, especially, become more isolated, a dog as a companion provides necessary emotional security. So, just as they love and protect us, we love and protect our dogs. We make sure they get the best of medical care, the best nutrition, the best of everything.

In a 2001 NPR talk show, Michael Fox, DVM, author of many excellent books on holistic veterinary practice and animal behavior, shocked his interviewer, Ray Suarez, and other guests by stating emphatically that pets are as important as children and other family members. Actually, he implied that they are *more* important. When questioned, he explained they are more faithful, supportive, non-judgmental, and forgiving than humans – especially relatives. They demonstrate their superhuman qualities 24-7.

Dogs are living longer now. They are kept indoors more, away from danger and predators. As they age, dogs develop the same infirmities that many people experience as they age. They now present with glaucoma, emphysema, liver disease, cancers and kidney disorders. This is in addition to the osteoarthritis, generalized joint stiffness and unexplained pains that are the result of a lifetime of wear and tear on the body and the spirit.

By learning to massage your dogs, you may not actually reverse your dog's aging process (although we've seen numerous examples of older or injured dogs who, after being practically at death's door, feel so much better that they romp and play like healthy 5-year olds), you will surely be able to slow it down. Your dog's inevitable decline will be more comfortable - more tolerable - more graceful.

Energy work is an extension of the PetMassage$_{TM}$ learned in our earlier courses. You will develop greater insight into the massage process when you understand the dynamics that occur between you and your dog as your two energetic bodies unite. The skills (tools) that you'll learn in this course are ones that you can easily use and add to your practice.

We are seeing a great upsurge of interest in PetMassage$_{TM}$. Now, when I give presentations at dog shows, I no longer feel I have to convince anyone that what we are teaching is important. It is a lot more comfortable and fun to preach to those who already believe. Wherever I give presentations and demonstrations, there are now wonderfully supportive crowds.

PetMassage$_{TM}$ is a newly recognized vocation. Many reporters have never heard of it. When they do, bells and whistles go off in their minds as they consider all the great stories they can write. After all, they all learned in school that the story "Dog Bites Man" isn't news, but when it's "Man Bites Dog," well, that's a story. This is a "Man Helps Dog" story. So be ready for media interviews.

As I was setting up my booth at the International Kennel Club Show in Chicago, a writer and photographer approached me from the Chicago Sun Times. He asked me "Which dogs need a massage?" I said, "All dogs need a massage." He asked me about the benefits. I rattled off a bunch of "quotables" and this is how the article about the show began in the paper the next morning:

The following two articles appeared in the Chicago Tribune, February 22, 2002 Section 5, Tempo Section and the Chicago Sun Times, Metro Section, Sunday, Feb. 25, 2002.

Chicago Tribune, February 22, 2002 Section 5, Tempo Section

*McCormick Place gone to the dogs,* **by Lucio Guerrero and Tim Novak**

"Every dogs needs a massage," according to Jonathan Rudinger.

And for $1 a minute the Toledo, Ohio man was giving rubdowns Saturday to the show dogs at McCormick Place this weekend for the International Kennel Club show. The show continues today from 8 to 5.

"We've probably done 75 dogs in the last three days, " Rudinger said, pitching his audio and video tapes on canine massage."

"Massage maintains wellness," he said. "It helps flexibility. It helps with reduced pain, with arthritis. It's human-animal bond. It helps dogs get through the emotional issues, like grieving."

And believe it or not, Rudinger said some of the pets he massages are owned by humans who've never had a rubdown.

"Some people value their dogs more than themselves."   About 40,000 people who value dogs attended the show Saturday. It's the largest bench show in the country where common people can get close to about 6,000 purebred dogs in 150 categories. Everything from grooming to feeding is open to the public....

Chicago Sun Times, Metro Section, Sunday, Feb. 25, 2002

**Kennel Club show breeds novel ways to put on the dog,** by William Hageman
**...Learning experience**
"Check out Jonathan Rudinger. Watch him. Listen to him. Take notes. Visit his website (www.petmassage.com). Your dog will love you for it. Rudinger is the founder and executive director of the PetMassage Training and Research Institute of Toledo, Ohio. He will be giving pet massage demonstrations at the Purina Dog Team area and working on show dogs at his own booth.

This is more than rubbing little Spanky behind the ears and watching him get glassy-eyed as a goofy dog grin crosses his muzzle.

"We combine the aspects of human massage, the Swedish form, which is long stroking, and petrissage, which is deep kneading, with acupressure and some more alternative forms of [massage]," Rudinger says.

And dogs love it. Well, most dogs.

"There are huge variations within breeds," he says. "I mean, I've worked with Chihuahuas that are lovely and wonderful, and then I've had Chihuahua's that have tried to attack me."

Not a pretty picture. Still, out of the thousands of dogs Rudinger, a former Loop art gallery owner, has worked on, he has never been bitten, "but I've come close."

The massage benefits dogs of all ages, Rudinger says. And they can help smooth over the rough spots. You don't really think about it, but dogs do a lot of grieving," he says. "Say you have a kid turn 18 and leave for college. When that child leaves, the dog really does grieve that loss of the child from the home. So dogs have a lot of emotional stuff. [A massage] puts them in a frame of mind where they can make a connection between their mind and body. It's a lot of comforting, a lot of holding, the touch."
####

# Unit 1
# This Course

# Chapter 1
## PetMassage™ Home-Study Course #2

### General Statement of Purpose & Vision for this Course

Many people believe that if they rub their dog's body they are giving him a massage. In the most limited sense, they are. The difference between that and the information taught in this course is similar to the difference between your getting a back rub from your child and a treatment from a professional massage therapist. Your son or daughter's touch may feel great and may even work out some of the kinks in your shoulder. But, the work you receive from someone who has been trained in this skill, will be more focused, intentional, specific, and therapeutic. When each touch has a reason for its movement, direction and focus; when each stroke has intention and purpose; when each session assists your dog to physical, behavioral and emotional enhancement, then you are practicing PetMassage™.

Massage is a tactile skill. The best way to learn it is one-on-one with an instructor.

That way, you can get one-on-one instruction to fine-tune your body mechanics and sensitiveness' to energy. The information in this course is an elaboration of one of the modules of our 7-day Advanced Workshop. If you have already attended one of the workshops, this course will expand on that experience.

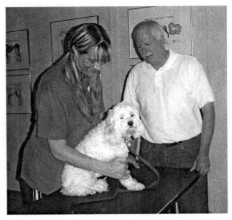

*Students receive individualized instruction in workshops*

2

If you cannot attend the workshop, this canine PetMassage$_{TM}$ course will support your continued learning.

The prerequisites needed to take the certification test for this course are either

- The PetMassage$_{TM}$ for Dogs  Home Study Course and/or
- The PetMassage$_{TM}$ for Dogs Foundation Workshop

A Certificate of Course Completion will be awarded upon submission of a written test, documentation of 12 canine massage/energy sessions, the course evaluation form, certificate application and payment of matriculation fees.

The PetMassage Energy Work with Dogs Course has four objectives:

1) To increase your awareness of the flow of energy, or life force
2) Discover and understand what "energy" is and how to experience it.
3) Develop skills to use this awareness to help animals: for the purpose of enhancing their energy quotient.
4) Enable pet caregivers to take better care of their dogs.
5) Spread the knowledge of PetMassage$_{TM}$ theories and techniques.

As we've indicated, just knowing how to rub your dog is not performing PetMassage$_{TM}$. We hear these wherever we go, "I rub my dog all the time and he just loves it. I'm already doing massage."

We start with the premise that practically every pet owner already knows how to touch and rub their dogs. We all love our dogs. We joyfully express our emotions by hugging and caressing them. When we are teaching a course, it's often difficult to keep students' hands off them between instruction periods. Each and every PetMassage™ stroke, as we shall learn, is mindful and purposeful. This itself separates the PetMassage™ form from idly rubbing and scratching your dog. Scratching him behind the ears or rubbing his belly is not massage therapy. It may feel good. It may relax him. But, it is not PetMassage™.

PetMassage™ combines the theories and techniques of several disciplines into a cohesive and effective form that is easy to learn and fun to practice. Studying this book and its accompanying audio version will help you to develop the skills to help your dogs realize their highest levels of healthfulness. You will gain understanding of practice and the theories behind this massage form. In all, you will have the skills to give a complete PetMassage™ Energy session.

The ultimate goals for this course will be for you to understand the concepts about energy and, more importantly, the answers to these two questions:

1) What is it?
2) How can I use this energy and awareness in my practice?

## Format of text

Each chapter contains a lecture portion and exercises, or practical applications.

Spend some time reflecting on and playing with the exercises, at the end of the chapters.

The exercises combine to create a separate course to help you to develop your skills of sensing energy and putting energy work into practice. They are, by themselves, a course on developing energy awareness.

| |
|---|
| The exercises at the end of the chapters are important. and these text boxes highlight important points. |

4

## Exercise 1: Observing energy

Start by sitting quietly, observing your breath.

Allow your attention to focus on your right hand. As you rotate your wrist, flex and extend your outstretched fingers. Feel the intricate interactions of the bones and muscles in your hand and wrist. Feel the movement begin in your forearms and elbows and radiate to your fingers.

With your attention on your forearm, sense the two long bones of your forearm, your radius and ulna. Visualize them glowing. As you turn your arm over to the prone position and back to supine, visualize the long bones gliding over each other. In your mind, *see and feel* pulses of light moving back and forth from wrist to elbow.

## Chapter 2

## The PetMassage~TM~ Scope of Practice

For those of you who are studying this and believe that when you've finished you can run right out and start massaging every dog you see, this section may be a little sobering. PetMassage~TM~ as a business needs to be practiced legally and comfortably. It is important to establish some parameters for our practice.

There are several activities that our scope does not include. Our scope does **not** include: diagnosing (identifying, naming) or treating specific physical imbalances. These are the provenance of veterinarians. And we are not practicing veterinary medicine. So when a dog is brought to you and it is showing obvious signs and symptoms of dysplastic hips or has large, solid, immovable lumps under his coat that you think might be tumors, it is not your place to identify what you are seeing. You may say that you detect a lump or a hardened area, but defining it with a name, is making a diagnosis and that is better done by someone with years of professional veterinary training: a vet. If you do detect anything while working on a dog that concerns you, you can describe what you have found to the dog's owner, suggesting that a vet be consulted. That's fine. That's encouraged. That's working in a healthy collegial role with that dog's veterinarian.

So, can we diagnose? No.

Can we treat specific diseases? No.

Can we recommend medications or diet changes? Medications? No. That would be practicing veterinary medicine without either the training or a license. Food? Maybe. Dog food is, for the most part, unregulated. There are many well-informed and well-intentioned dog food products. At dog shows and pet stores, manufacturers' reps appear to be the authorities on diet. At least that's what they'd like us to believe. Each puts her own spin on what's best for your dog and is eager to tell you why whatever you are currently feeding your dog is inferior to whatever they are selling. If you can bring a modicum of calm and common sense to the conversation about nutrition, then there is a place for you in counseling. We will learn that each dog is unique and has unique needs. These include not only massage, but also nutrition and supplements. Some do best with kibble, some with raw food. Dogs' needs and requirements change as they move through their stages of life.

Many dogs thrive with the aid of flower essence therapy, for example, while others pay no heed to it. Their response to all the fuss is, "Whatever." PetMassage™ focus is on touch and its application. We do not include diet and nutrition in our scope of practice.

Can we claim to heal? No. However... we <u>can</u> assist dogs in their self-healing. And, we <u>can</u> refer clients to other professionals whose work we admire and trust.

The use of magnets is still open to discussion. Many people swear by them claiming they have helped their dogs and horses. Others swear at them claiming they are over hyped. We do not use magnets in PetMassage™ practice. PetMassage™ work is to be done with our hands and our spirits. It is the connection of our energetic bodies that is important. If you are one who finds value in their use, by all means, continue with them. Use them between sessions, but certainly not during them.

Most vets have neither the time nor the training to provide massage to their patients. Complete sessions often last over 30 minutes. In a busy clinic, that would be too time consuming for the doctor. The techniques we teach *complement* the fine work already being done by veterinarians.

Precise language is important here. Note that we did not use the term "alternative." "Alternative" would imply *a substitution* or work that is "instead of" veterinary care. "Complementary to" and "integrative with" are more appropriate descriptions of our service regarding veterinarians and other health care professionals. Our work *is* a complement to and integrates with holistic and traditional veterinary care.

> PetMassage$_{TM}$ complements both traditional and holistic veterinary care.

I can foresee that in the near future, animal massage therapists will play a major supporting role in the pre - and post - surgery rehabilitation as well as the wellness maintenance of animals. The role of animal massage practitioners will have a similar role to that of human massage therapists, physical therapists and physical therapy assistants for people.

**Teaching Owners vs. giving PetMassages to dogs**
We've found that many pet owners often will stop scheduling appointments for their dogs after 4 or 5 sessions. Even though they acknowledge that their dogs benefit from massage, time, money, and/or scheduling (life) become excuses for discontinuing their dogs' massage treatments.

If, in the same 4 or 5 sessions, we can *teach* dogs' owners to give massages, they will have the option to continue the therapy at home. Dogs won't have to wait weeks until their next appointment. They will at least have the potential for getting the daily therapy with all its benefits. That would certainly be best for their dogs. Owners often soon realize that their pets aren't the only ones benefiting. They soon learn that in many ways they get a lot out of PetMassage$_{TM}$, too.

At the time of this writing, in most states, even those trained in animal massage cannot legally massage pets. Only licensed veterinarians, those working under veterinary supervision, and the private owners of the pets can "perform manipulations as therapy," i.e., massage. Just to make sure that you are practicing legally, you may want to check with your state or municipal codes and laws. One place to check is to request a copy of your state's Veterinary Scope of Practice. At the very least, you can learn what you need to know so that you will not be accused of practicing veterinary medicine without a license.

Teaching PetMassage$_{TM}$, we have the opportunity to train the owners of dogs, vets and vet techs the PetMassage$_{TM}$ techniques.

**An ounce of prevention…**
Eventually, we will all catch on to the concept that prevention is a lot more effective than treating a medical or emotional problem after the fact.

PetMassage$_{TM}$ is complementary to all home health maintenance programs. Whether it is used immediately after a traumatic episode, or while your dog is still in prime condition, massage and energy work are very effective techniques to maintain and extend your dog's *quality of life*.

In the past several years, medical doctors have begun to acknowledge that their human patients benefit from massage therapy. The relaxation and muscle toning effects of massage are well documented. It has become evident that some form of massage/energy or bodywork can be helpful in practically every physical condition. The mind-body connection has become well established too. Massage therapy for people, has become an accepted complement to traditional, allopathic medical care.

As we have shown, PetMassage$_{TM}$ is complementary to both traditional and holistic medical/veterinary care. Now veterinarians are discovering this, too. And we are not only talking about the holistic vets who use herbs, natural supplements and acupuncture in their practices. More traditional, old school vets are also recognizing the many benefits their patients get from massage.

Several traditionally schooled vets have confided with us that in their competitive practices, they see the writing on the wall: they must include holism in their practice if their business is to survive. "It is what the dog owner demands," says one vet. "

They are no longer satisfied with the prescription drugs that used to suffice."

These vets are now either attending our workshops themselves or sending their techs to learn PetMassage$_{TM}$. They can proudly claim to now offer a greater range of services…programs that include massage therapy for their patients.

**Legal Restrictions.**

At the time of this writing, many states' legislatures have written very comprehensive veterinary scopes of practice into the laws. In them, only licensed veterinarians, people working directly under their supervision and the owners of dogs can perform manipulations on animals for the purposes of therapy.

This is changing. States' legislators are becoming more enlightened and are understanding that if untrained owners can massage their dogs, then it makes sense that non-vet persons who have had specialized training in animal massage ought to be able to therapeutically massage animals. They would be professional in their work. They would certainly be better than those without training.

PetMassage_TM is compatible with every known form of wellness care: PetMassage_TM techniques are gentle and effective. We teach owners to work on their own dogs. We work with our students to develop skills of understanding the special needs of their animals and supporting the self-healing of theses special needs through the use of knowledgeable, compassionate touch, positional release, acupressure, energy balancing and gentle fascia releases. We do not diagnose or treat specific disorders, prescribe medications or recommend specific dietary regimens.

Until then, our niche is to teach our PetMassage™ techniques to veterinarians, other pet professionals such as vet techs, vet assistants, groomers, trainers and pet owners.

**Exercise 2**
**Observing your center**

Start by sitting quietly, observing your breath. Stand and place your feet shoulder width apart, slightly soften your knees, keeping your back vertical. Center your weight between your toes and your heels and between your feet for a few moments until you feel yourself set and balanced.

Slowly shift your weight from your toes to your heels and back. Shift your weight from one side to the other. Do this gradually. Start with your weight evenly distributed between your two feet and legs 50% to 50%. Move to 55% to 45%, 60%-40%, all the way to 5% to 95%. Your open foot should just be lightly resting on the floor. Hold this posture. Feel the lightness (emptiness) of your open leg and foot.

Feel the fullness and anchoring of your leg and foot. Lift the empty foot just off the ground and feel your total weight balanced on your "full" leg and foot. You are centered over your stabilizing foot. Slowly transfer your center back to the middle. Pause, and move your center over to the other side. Lift your empty leg, balancing your weight on you "full" leg. Place it back onto the ground. Observe your body as you slowly shift back to center.

Chapter 3
Definitions

**Basic Massage, definitions**:
Definitions for massage vary in their views, contexts, and parameters. We shall look at a few of them to see what they reveal about their underlying philosophies and motivations and then we'll see how each of them applies to PetMassage$_{TM}$ Energy Work.

Basic Swedish massage, with its Western medical orientation has this definition:

the manipulation of muscles and skin to promote increased circulation to all the organs and tissues in the body, [Kellogg]

The focus for medical massage is on touching with varying amounts of pressure and the physical response from that touch. If you press onto your arm with your thumb or finger, for example, and then release the pressure, you'll see a faint residual mark. Your skin will quickly return to its normal color. What you've done is press the blood out of the capillaries closest to the surface of the skin.

When you remove the pressure, your blood flows back into the blood vessels. You have just manipulated the skin and the connective tissue under it, affecting circulation. The movements are mechanical and the results, predictable. In the home study course #1 we learned the various strokes and their effects on the movements

*Oskar gets a lick in*

of blood, lymph, cerebral spinal fluid, and all the other fluids in the body.

Another definition is the manipulation of the soft tissue of the body through stroking, rubbing, kneading, or tapping, to increase circulation, and to improve muscle tone, and to relax the recipient. (Mosby's Medical Dictionary, 4th Ed).

The focus is on the effects of various types of touch: stroking, rubbing, kneading and tapping. Increased circulation with the intent of improving muscle tone creates a state of relaxation. The concept of relaxation refers to the softening of muscle tissue, connective tissue (fascia), ligaments and tendons. Decreasing strain or intensity of fascia tightness is the mechanical result of skilled touch. The feeling of total body wellness is the emotional effect of relaxing the physical elements.

We know that by using stimulation stroking, distal to proximal, against   the natural grain of the coat (frictioning, rubbing, kneading and tapping), we can warm the muscles and skin by drawing blood to the surface. Then, with a combination of assistive and resistive range of motion (ROM), massage can increase flexibility and enhances muscle tone.

Connective tissue is tissue that supports and connects other tissues and tissues and parts (Taber's® Cyclopedic Medical Dictionary, 16th Edition). One particular connective tissue requires special attention. It is the tissue called fascia. Fascia is so significant that entire forms of massage therapy have focused on it. You have most likely heard of myofascia release, or the "structural" integration of Rolfing. These were developed to rebalance and reprogram the fascia in the body that has become strained and distorted.

Fascia is defined as the "fibrous tissue between muscle bundles that support nerves and blood vessels" [Beck] It is throughout the body, wherever there is muscle tissue and blood, which is pretty much everywhere.

To give you an idea of how pervasive fascia is in our and our dogs' bodies, consider a muscle cell. Surrounding this cell is a thin layer of fascia. A group of muscle cells combine to form a muscle fibril, which is surrounded by a layer of fascia. It holds the cells together. Muscle fibrils are bound together to form muscle fibers. The fibers are bound together to form muscles. The muscles are bound together to form muscle groups. Each are held together with fascia. The ends of the outer coverings of muscle groups combine and connect the muscles to bones. This highly concentrated fascia is called a tendon.

A couple of examples of fascia that you can see and feel are the tough filmy substances under the skin of a raw chicken leg or the film inside an eggshell. Fascia has been metaphorically described as plastic wrap supporting and containing the muscles under the skin, around and in muscle tissue.

There is also fascia just beneath the surface of your dog's skin, covering his superficial muscles. With movement or stress, this wrap can become twisted or bunched. A skewed arrangement of fascia causes limitations of his movement and accompanying discomfort. The normal patterns of healthy fascia are often disrupted as the result of injury, surgery, and/or repetitive motion, such as always turning in one direction. When these limitations persist, a *holding pattern* is created. PetMassage$_{TM}$ works on a physical level to smooth and unbind stuck fascia, allowing dogs more freedom of movement. Traumas and stresses are often bound into the fibers of their bodies.

We each have a tendency to gasp and hold in our breath during anxious moments or when experiencing pain. Building up pressure strains the diaphragm, the record of your anxiety, gets encoded into the fascia of muscle tissue. This is how anxiety is the cause of discomfort and reduced range of motion. This is why traumatic experiences, can be the root cause of such debilitating behaviors as minor muscle spasms, asthma and seizures.

Anxiety as an emotion is accessed through PetMassage_TM Energy Work. During his session, you assist your dog in connecting with memory. Your dog unconsciously identifies and may choose to heal the causative memory. Release of the cause releases its hold on the body. As the holds on the body continue to unwind, they release more of the tied-up fascia. The body unwinds to more comfort and greater range of motion, ROM. This is an explanation of the dynamics of how bodywork affects the body.

Holding patterns have behavioral effects, too. By releasing the causative memories trapped in the fascia, we are assisting the dog to more healthy ROE, Range of Emotion. This can help dogs with socializing as well as training issues.

Here are two other definitions:
One of our PetMassage_TM workshop students described it as, "Massage is a harmonious connection with your pet."
This will make more sense as we continue.

The definition of massage, as "touching the physical and *energetic body* with a *healing      purpose,"* (Schwartz, Dr. C. , Four Paws Five Directions) expands in two ways on the concept of mechanistically working the muscles and skin to affect circulation. Integral in this definition is the holistic inclusion of the "energetic body" as an integral part of the whole body. And, it acknowledges the influence of "purpose." This mind-body connection is essential for successful energy bodywork.

**Exercise 3**
**Bonding**

Sit quietly with your dog. Place both hands on his body, one on the croup, the other either under the neck or over the withers. Observe your breath. Gently palpate your dog's body. Closely observe the contours, shapes and textures of your dog's head, shoulders, legs, topline, ribs, abdomen and tail.

Observe with your eyes; studying the patterns in the hair, the sheen of the coat, and the light in the eyes. With your nose, assess any unusual or pungent odors in the coat, mouth and ears. Observe with your hands. How does the coat feel? How about the webbing between the toes; the cheek and gums? How does your dog respond to your touch? Do you feel closer, more bonded, now? Having experienced this session, do you think your dog's relationship with you has changed?

Chapter 4
Physical and Energetic Body

It is important to know what is happening under your hands. Your dog's responses are happening in his coat, skin, connective tissue, fatty tissues, muscles, tendons, ligaments, joint capsules, bones and organ systems. His entire body reacts to your touch. His fundamental physical systems processing inside him are his digestive, circulatory, cardiovascular, respiratory, neurological, lymphatic and muscular. In other words, his processes are similar to your human anatomy and physiology. To be effective, you need to have a solid general education of canine body parts and systems.

The system that establishes and maintains balance and coordination within all the other systems is the system of dynamic energy movement. The term "Ch'i" is used to describe this energy.

Although we refer to and work on muscle

> Breathe.

groups such as the hamstrings, pectorals and intercostals, we find it unnecessary to spend a lot of time and effort learning the specific names of all muscles, their origins and insertion sites, actions, etc. In PetMassage_TM Energy Work, once you have a basic awareness of how the dog's body functions, there is less emphasis on pure anatomy and physiology.

If however, you believe that knowing the Latin medical terminology will make you a better therapist, then, by all means learn as much as you can. If that is the direction you would like to go, you will find this information in our charts and other books available in our PetMassage_TM Institute bookstore and website.

It is difficult to distinguish between the physical and the energetic bodies. When we use these terms it separates aspects of one holistic living organism into two. Each can neither exist nor function without the other. In this discussion, we will be referring to each separately, but the bottom line is, it is all about the energy. It is all about the movement, the connections and flow. It is about the maintenance of balance among, within, around and through the body.

The concept of "purpose," is significant. The first questions that come to mind are whose purpose and what purpose?

It is with the dog's purpose that we are primarily concerned. The reason we are working with them is to enhance quality of life. We get feel-good rewards, too. They are bountiful, fun, exciting, and yet secondary to the benefits received by our dogs.

## Exercise 4
## Walking meditation

Start by sitting quietly, observing your breath. Stand and place your feet shoulder width apart, slightly soften your knees, keeping your back vertical. Center your weight between your toes and your heels and between your feet for a few moments until you feel yourself set and balanced.

Slowly shift your weight from your toes to your heels and back. Shift your weight from one side to the other. Do this gradually. Start with your weight evenly distributed between your two feet and legs 50% to 50%. Move to 55% to 45%, 60%-40%, all the way to 5% to 95%. Your open foot should just be lightly resting on the floor. Hold this posture. Feel the lightness (emptiness) of your open leg and foot.

Feel the fullness and anchoring of your leg and foot with the weight. Lift the empty foot just off the ground and feel your total weight balanced on your "full" leg and foot. You are centered over your stabilizing foot. Place your empty foot about 12 inches in front and 12 inches to the side. Slowly transfer your weight onto this foot, making it the full one and the other, the empty. Slowly and thoughtfully move about transferring your weight from one foot to the other. Continue your walking meditation for 5 minutes. Remember to breathe as you move about.

# Unit 2
# Benefits

Chapter 5
The Benefits - Physical

Let's review some of the more obvious benefits that dogs get from PetMassage<sub>TM</sub> Energy work.

**PetMassage<sub>TM</sub> Energy Work helps to assess and maintain wellness.**
PetMassage<sub>TM</sub> techniques are skills you can use to enhance your dog's quality of life. Maintaining daily or weekly assessments of your dog's condition, you can identify and react quickly and efficiently to any unusual sign or symptom that you detect. This is wellness maintenance. If you detect anything that concerns you, call your vet.

The rituals of your PetMassage<sub>TM</sub> energy sessions often develop into special sharing times that your dog will enjoy and anticipate with eagerness. Each session is a special event! This shared nurturing time in itself, will enhance your dog's level of wellness. Several former students have lamented that they now have to factor

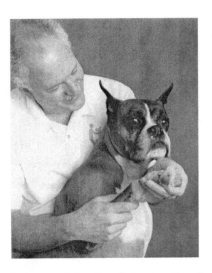

*Oskar anticipating "sharing time"*

an extra half hour into their morning routine because their dogs won't let them out of the bathroom until they've had massages.

Many dogs have participated in our PetMassage<sub>TM</sub> research projects that involved several weeks of sessions. Their owners tell us that by the 3$^{rd}$ session, dogs are so eager for the treatments that they wait by the front door and eagerly bound to the car for their ride to the PetMassage$_{TM}$ Institute. By the time they pull into the parking lot, the dogs have already begun their therapy.

PetMassage$_{TM}$ energy sessions can also be palliative. That is, they can be comforting and supportive when actual physical help is no longer an option. This work helps dogs make their transitions from this life form to the next. It benefits the ones who are saying goodbye, as well. It is a vehicle for acceptance and release.

**Increases circulation**

One aspect of PetMassage$_{TM}$ is pushing and pulling, rubbing and stretching the surfaces of the body. We create and support movement at the joints through assistive and resistive Range of Motion (ROM). We will learn techniques that can be used to enhance the circulation of Ch'i throughout the body, enhancing the balance of the flow of all bodily fluids.

People already know how to rub their dogs. As pet owners it's often a challenge to keep our hands off them. The technical parts of massage can be taught in a weekend. The study of PetMassage$_{TM}$ as a methodology, takes practice, time - time in the saddle, and patience. Once you've learned the skills of using your hands, body and spirit to connect with your dog, you can focus on the whys and wherefores. The most important parts of the massage process are happening inside your dog.

You are supporting the connection of your dog's *mind, body and spirit*. This *mind, body, and spirit* phrase has become a New Age mantra, kind of like "Peace and Love" in the 1960's, or "Have a Nice Day" in the 1970's. PetMassage$_{TM}$ assists dogs in making these fundamental connections.

Your dog will follow on the inside wherever your hands touch on the outside. As his attention moves to each spot you touch, his body awareness is enhanced. His attention is drawn to the different points on his body as you progress through the massage. Your dog becomes more alert.

He also follows the depth of your touch. Touch lightly; his attention is on the surface. Press in a little more; his attention is on the fascia just beneath the coat. Press deeper; he'll begin to feel the bony structures and shapes of his muscles, ligaments and tendons. His attention flows to whichever level you touch.

His energy flows not just within the body, but it is also outside it. Just as you can sometimes tell when someone is standing behind you, your dog too, can sense the sensation of presence. Hold your hand 12 inches from his body. He is aware that you have accessed his personal space. His self-body tracking increases his conscious mental circulation. It increases his body awareness. This is known as proprioception.

Who knows what dogs think about? We can be sure that dogs are acutely aware of body language. They connect with the movements of our hands around their bodies. They understand the messages of touch. They react to how they are touched, the quality of the connection, how much they are touched, and the intention behind your touch.

Hold your arm over your dog's withers; he will automatically understand your body language to establish yourself as the more dominant member of his pack. Make direct eye contact; he will automatically focus on which of you is the more dominant.

Dogs' abilities to cognate their bodies are amazing. A dog can feel a fly when it lands on his coat. He knows when a mosquito lands on him. Since he is aware of these insects, he will certainly feel your every touch. Using techniques that are very light, accessing just the surface or working off his body with intention,

PetMassage<sub>TM</sub> energy work can calm overly excited animals, rouse apathetic ones and comfort those who are upset.

You are helping to rebalance circulation. That is, his physical *and* mental *and* spiritual circulation.

---

Experiencing what your dog will receive.
*"For what we are about to receive,
let us be thankful."*

---

Incredibly enough, many of the students who have traveled to attend our workshops, investing their time and money, have never themselves received a professional full body massage. These are intelligent and caring people who understand on a cerebral level how beneficial massage therapy must be, but who have never themselves experienced the effects of a professional full body massage. Without personal experience of their own responses to massage, they cannot recognize the levels they need to respond to in supporting their dogs' massage experience.

An essential part of their workshop experience then, is to receive massage. This experience is necessary. Until they have experienced massage and know what energy work is and feels like, they will never understand how profound the experience of touch can be. They will never be able to project the intention of healing in their sessions.

As a practitioner of PetMassage<sub>TM</sub>, you need to know what it means and why it is important to have the *intentionality* to access, witness and support those spaces where healing can happen. If you are reading this and have never received a professional full-body massage, pause here, bookmark this page. Call a massage therapist, make an appointment and go get a massage. Schedule a full hour, if you can. You are worth the little extra cost. A half hour session is okay; a full hour will give your body and spirit time to relax. Receive and have this experience integrate into your body, mind and spirit. We'll still be here when you get back.

> Until they have experienced and know what it feels like, they will never understand just how profound is the experience of touch.

"Massage and muscle therapy are very beneficial throughout your dogs' performance years. Massage increases blood flow and nutrition to the working muscles, as well as carrying waste and by-products away. Massage and stretching are essential before and after work-outs. Massage can also be very beneficial in healing injuries as it can decrease the amount of scar tissue build up and decrease the healing time." (Dr. C. J. Farren, D.C., Hillsdale, IL)

> It is important to have the *intention* to access, witness and support those spaces where healing can happen.

## Exercise 5
## Ch'i Gung form centering

Stand with your feet about shoulder length apart. Point your toes either outward or inward, whichever is more comfortable. Slightly relax and bend your knees. You'll want to have your knees over and pointing in the direction of your toes. Flatten your back, tilting your pelvis upward slightly. Breathe easily in this position, observing the movement of air into and out of your throat, chest and abdomen. Watch your belly inflate with your inhalation and deflate with your exhalation.

Inhalation: Start with your hands down by your sides. Imagine yourself scooping up handfuls of energy around your knees and thighs. With a long slow inhalation, bring your hands (with their energy) up, following - but not touching - the contours of your body high above your head. Move to a slow steady count from one to ten on the inhalation.

Exhalation: With a long slow count down from ten to one, exhale, bringing your hands down, again following the contours of your head and torso.

Feel the tingling feeling of the movement of energy as your hands pass over your body. Feel the sense of centeredness and grounding. Use this form before every animal massage session. It feels cleansing and grounding. It balances and totally focuses your attention – your mind, body and spirit – on the present situation.

Chapter 6
Flexibility and Strength

**PetMassage<sub>TM</sub> strengthens the body by stimulating the muscles.**
We've all heard the phrase "Use it or lose it." It's true.
Stimulating muscles works them. PetMassage<sub>TM</sub> helps to maintain muscle and tissue tone. Massage is especially important for older dogs who are not getting enough exercise; it can be used to keep their joints supple. Ten minutes of vigorous massage is worth an hour's walk.

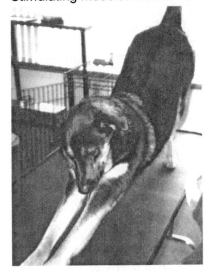

*Stretching*

PetMassage<sub>TM</sub> also helps recirculate blood and energy to areas that are not being used such as joints that are kept immobile due to splints or post surgical pain.

PetMassage<sub>TM</sub> is important for dogs recovering from surgery who are guarding—and not using an affected limb.

**Massage restores flexibility.**
Older or injured dogs who experience joint pain with movement often restrict their movements to avoid any discomfort. In this way they act just like humans. If it hurts to move their limb, it simply won't be moved. If it hurts to put weight on one foot, it is easy enough to hop around on the other three. By gently frictioning affected areas, warming the skin and connective

tissue, with vigorous strokes using assistive and resistive ROM and by getting the joints themselves to respond during positional release, flexibility is gently and gradually increased.

The key to eliciting an unwinding response is to keep your movement gentle, loving and focused.

PetMassage$_{TM}$ enhances your dog's mental flexibility too. While in a parasympathetic state of consciousness, dogs recall what it feels like to function with less discomfort. They remember how their bodies felt and moved when they were in their prime. We often think that dogs only live in the present. But behavioral modeling shows us that they have vivid memories and can entrain their bodies with their memories (minds eye). In the same vein, your dog's holding patterns may be behavioral in nature. Much of his behavior is learned, both well socialized and dysfunctional. And, the memory of his experiences or lessons, are stored in his muscles, and connective tissue. Release the stuckness in his body and he releases the memories stored in there. So, the root causes of dysfunctional behavior can also be released to allow them to behave in more healthy ways.

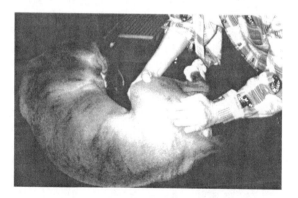

*Working Oskar's sore, stiff hip*

As dogs develop better muscle tone, their bodies become more flexible, more symmetrical; their movements have more joy, grace and balance. They can walk without limping or tripping and run without roaching their backs or side-winding. Older and post-surgical dogs can often regain the ease of movement that they only vaguely recall having.

**Helps older dogs and post-surgery dogs cope with the stiffness and discomfort that accompanies arthritis.**
Massage therapy helps reduce the pain and stiffness of osteoarthritis. The process of warming the tissues with friction and petrissage, deep kneading, softens the fascia beneath the skin, reducing muscular knots and spasms. Retained fluids resorb easily back into tissues.

Endorphins, the body's own natural opiates, or pain-killers, are released into the blood stream during the stimulation of massage. So, by softening the tissue, reducing the edema (swelling, inflammation) and allowing his body to give itself a mild pain reliever, it's easy to understand how your arthritic dog becomes more comfortable and more mobile. In addition to the kneading strokes, which work on your dog's superficial tissues and fascia, we use gentle exploration of movement routines. These help your dog to break through the stiffness of calcified joints and stuck fascia easily and willingly. His quality of life requires greater ease of movement.

There is a definite distinction between PetMassage™ and the work of physical therapy. Whereas PT will focus on repetitive exercises to enhance the structure and functioning of specific muscle groups, and this is important and necessary work too, PetMassage™ addresses the entire dog as a whole, unified system. Dogs' bodies are so interconnected that to work on just the shoulder or hip, as examples, would not be a satisfying experience for the dog, nor would it be effective as a whole body therapy.

We will learn about the corner–to–corner response and how each part of your dog's body is facilitated and supported by every other part of his anatomy.  All the limbs and body systems that have been overworked from compensating for weight and stress and guarding from pain need to be supported, too.

One of the muscles that requires the most attention is the diaphragm.  This is the primary breathing muscle. Its movement alternates the pressures within the body cavity to maintain the flow of lymph, so it is called the lymphatic pump. It is the internal regulator of your dog's *hara*, his center of power, his source of intention. Just as we people tend to hold our breath when in pain, so do dogs.  When the rhythmic pattern of breathing, the constant massage of the hara, is interrupted, the internal flow of Ch'i is thrown out of balance. Breath is important to maintain our dogs' quality of life.

**Helps dogs relate to sense of "perfect" self**
Dogs usually have pretty well-developed senses of self. They know who they are. They understand their placement within the order of their own species pack, their relationships with people, and other animals. They are acutely aware of each other's level of wellness and pack status. They are also aware of the state of their own healthfulness or wellness. They know themselves as they were designed to be, as their genetics designed them.

So, a dog whose leg has been amputated from disease or trauma would still recall his potential of running on all fours. A boxer that has had his tail cut and his ears trimmed would still have the self-image of being a dog with a naturally long tail and big floppy ears.  We'll see the importance of working between

31

each of the joints in the body, including the phantom joints on tails that have been docked. And there are acupoints on the edges of earflaps that can still be stimulated, even though they were cut long ago.

During the PetMassage$_{TM}$ session, your dog's phantom, or missing parts need to be acknowledged and massaged along with his physical self. This creates a complete session that values and supports the whole dog.

Recently, I observed an old dog as a puppy raced past him. He hauled himself up to his feet, jogged a couple of paces, stopped and slowly eased himself back down again. You could almost hear him thinking, as he watched the puppy run, "I'm not as young as I used to be. Wish I could run like that again!" His concept of his *perfect self* was to be as vital as his younger self.

During the PetMassage$_{TM}$ experience, each dog gets in touch with his individual concept of his perfect self. Holding this image in his mind (or on his unconscious level) he strives to become one with it. It becomes an inner visual and spiritual affirmation. The fractured leg can become whole; the malignant tumor can become healthy tissue.

At the end of life, your dog may strive to achieve another kind of perfection. He may opt for the comfort, beauty and balance that comes with the peace of death. Massage can also be used palliatively. That is, to provide comfort and support as he prepares to make his transition. In this case, PetMassage$_{TM}$ serves not only the dog, but also, just as importantly, his owner. It helps both to say, " Goodbye, peace be with you." It is also a way for you to give him permission to move on.

**PetMassage increases circulation.**
The increased blood flow helps alleviate pain and

removes build-up of a chemical called lactic acid. Lactic acid is produced as an end product of muscle work. As this chemical builds up, the muscles respond with fatigue and pain. It's the body's self-regulating apparatus that lets the muscles know when to stop. Massage therapists sometimes refer to the excess of this chemical as "toxins". This chemical is also the cause of next day soreness after strenuous exercise. Its presence is felt as muscle knots. One source poetically describes the tiny hardened bumps in the tissue as "marbles in the mud."

Cardio-vascular circulation helps move these chemicals out of the muscle tissue, into the venous blood system where they can be filtered out by the kidneys and excreted. PetMassage$_{TM}$ comforts tired muscles.

---

PetMassage$_{TM}$ comforts tired muscles.

---

**Exercise 6**
**Body language**

Hold your outstretched arm over and touching your dog's withers. What is his reaction? Hold your palm next to your dog's face. What is his reaction? Hold the back of your hand to your dog's face. What is his reaction?

Lie on your back on the floor and observe your dog's behavior. What is his reaction? Lie on your tummy on the floor. Get on your hands and knees. What are his reactions?

Chapter 7
Emotional and Behavioral

**PetMassage_TM affects behavioral issues. It relieves not only physical discomfort but emotional pain as well.**

A dog that has been abused or abandoned can relate to the time before he had experienced his emotional scarring. Wouldn't it be great to know what incidents in your dog's past created his neuroses and contributed to peculiar behaviors? Your dog remembers. Dogs are like us -- they have selective memories. We can train and train, click and click and eventually they will figure out

> Abused and abandoned dogs relate to the time before they experienced emotional scarring.

what we want them to learn. In contrast to all your positive reinforcement training, just one unpleasant experience can be the trigger for a lifetime of behavioral issues.

*Every dog craves routine and sameness*

PetMassage_TM Energy Work is especially effective in assisting dogs to work through their emotional baggage. During the PetMassage_TM experience, dogs get in touch with the memories of themselves when they were unscarred. Their perception of an environment gone crazy can find peace. The dog stuck in frantic helplessness is given permission to relax. The emotional self-healing helps dogs adapt to new life situations.

New people or animals may be introduced into their lives. New homes, different cars, new trees and parks, new diet, new methods of training are all challenges to every dog who craves routine and sameness. PetMassage$_{TM}$, you can see, helps dogs develop healthier patterns of behavior.

Dogs often react to the stimuli in situations through the filter of physical or emotional discomfort. If we have a headache, we don't want to be around anybody. If a dog is in pain, he is not inclined to be sociable either. Emotional pain is another filter that we all have to work through.

Dogs' primary issues stem from five main categories:
- Fear
- Uncertainty of pack status
- Abandonment
- Abuse
- Grieving

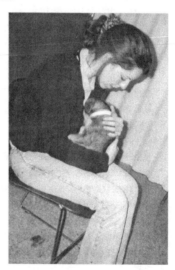

At the PetMassage$_{TM}$ Institute, we spend half a day of our Foundation workshops at our local Humane Society. The people who work there are some of the kindest, most loving and nurturing people I know and although they have the best of intentions and give their best in care, in reality, the dogs there are still reacting big time to each of the above issues. These filters can and will be addressed only with their

*These dogs will learn to trust*

adoption into secure and loving homes. Then, with time and routine, these dogs will learn to trust again.

**Fear**
In recent years, with the aid of such insightful books as *The Man Who Listens to Horses*, by Monty Roberts, we have come to understand

*Could it be…?*

that the flight or fight mechanism is the basis for understanding much of animal behavior and intercommunication. Dogs, like horses retreat from that which they fear and conversely, are drawn to and will work to achieve rewards. This is the basis of most of the more enlightened training methods being taught today.

**Abandonment**
Whether the dogs at the shelter have been tearfully surrendered, "dumped" by the side of a road, or just found lost and confused, all are feeling abandoned and unsupported.

Even as our students are giving them loving and nurturing massages, we can sense these dogs strain to hear every voice outside the door. We realize they are listening for familiar voices from their old lives. I tear up each time I watch a dog's head cock to one side with eyes and ears focused on some child's voice coming through the wall from the next room. Could it be…?

## Abuse

All these dogs are victims of some sort of abuse. Some have been physically beaten, chained or underfed. Some dogs are so overfed they can barely walk; that's another form of abuse. Some are infested with parasites. Some have been so harshly rooted trained that their

*20 minutes of PetMassage patience*

spirits have been broken. Some are so under trained they are clueless about appropriate social behavior. Some are healthy and beautiful, but with deeply emotional baggage. Some have been unlucky enough to be discarded like a piece of furniture when their owners moved into a new condo or apartment that didn't allow pets.

Some are so bored they pace, weave, incessantly jump or chew on their legs. All are undergoing the emotional stress that comes with transition. They have come from a place of knowing their role in their family to this new living environment. Some may appear confident and secure, but every one of them is uncertain of where he or she belongs and what is happening.

## Uncertainty of pack status

Fundamental to dogs' emotional well-being is awareness of their status in their pack. In kennel situations such as the Humane Society, dogs are often kept isolated in separate cages. They are in protective custody. They are given the best medical care, they are well fed, and well treated physically, but they are still pack animals and can only be truly comfortable when they've figured out their place in their social order.

Dog to dog aggression is common in the confusion. It's a foreign and strained social situation. "Who are these other dogs in the cages next to me and across the aisle?" Where do I belong in their pack?

They could be the top dog or place themselves somewhere else in the range of the pecking order. Wherever their place, they find solace in discovering where they belong.

**Grieving**
And they grieve. They miss the sights, the sounds, smells and all the wonderful human contact that made up the stuff of their old lives. These new sights and sounds and smells are all foreign and disorienting. When dogs grieve, they display similar sorts of behaviors as people experiencing loss.

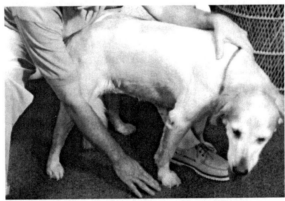

*Gracie before her massage*

Gracie, the lab-mix who was the recipient of the Geriatric Massage in the Effective PetMassage_TM for Older Dogs, DVD is a good example.

Before the massage, she stayed so close she was often touching her owner's side. Her eyes were dull. Her tail hung listlessly. Her head was carried low and her nose was down below her elbows. Her coat was dull and appeared rough and poorly clipped. Her breathing was shallow. Her movements were slow and lethargic.

*Gracie after her massage*

Some of the signs of grieving are:
1) Reduced energy
2) appearing listless
3) Tire more easily
4) Sleep more
5) Lose their appetite and lose weight

After her massage she was a different dog. Her head was up, her ears were pricked and forward, her eyes were alert and bright, her tail was up and wagging. She panted freely. The corners of her mouth pulled up into what resembled a smile.

Somewhere in the 30 or so minutes that we shared the massage experience, she was able to work through what had been troubling her. Oh, did I mention that earlier that week, her family companion of 9 years had been put down? Gracie had been grieving.

6) Coats become dull (with reduced circulation)
7) Eyes lose their brightness (with reduced interest)
8) Ears and tails hang loosely
9) They become more needy, having to be close or in contact most of the time; Velcro dogs
10) They also go through stages of grief similar to humans. They often progress to anger and acting out, resignation and hopefully, acceptance.

The effects of fear, abandonment, abuse and uncertainty of pack status are held within the muscles, tendons, organs and connective tissue in your dog's body. It is soft-wired into the neurological system. They are part of the sympathetic nervous system and, as such, are always wearing down, draining the energy from your dog's quality of life.

**PetMassage$_{TM}$ supports dogs in times of crisis: surgery, injury.**
There are many crisis events in which massage can help. Dogs, like humans, benefit when they are given PetMassage$_{TM}$ directly before and after surgery. The pre-op effects are similar to the effects of massage on humans. Our experience has been that they go into pre-op quieter and calmer.

Dogs are keenly tuned in to their owners' emotions. Their concerns, fears, anxieties and confidence levels as well, are all registered and amplified in their minds. When we have the owners massage dogs just prior to their being prepared for surgery, they will become more relaxed, empowered by being able to "do" something supportive rather than just waiting and worrying. As they calm themselves, their dogs quiet along with them as they progress through their massage "ritual." Dogs who respond to their owner's new level of confidence become more compliant patients. When the owner connects to her sense of comfort and safety through the ritual use of PetMassage$_{TM}$, her dog will feel the familiar sense of comfort and relief. The angst of the event will become easier for each to handle. PetMassage$_{TM}$ benefits both the dogs and their owners.

Having gone into the operation in a more relaxed state, dogs often come out of post-op quicker and recover from the entire event faster. When dogs are more relaxed, and respiratory function is enhanced,

they require less anesthesia. By increasing their circulation throughout their bodies, massage helps reduce the effects of the anesthesia used. The toxic drugs are resorbed into the blood stream more efficiently where they are filtered through the kidneys and excreted in the urine. Similar effects on humans are well documented. There is no reason to suggest that dogs' responses are different.

*Healing Touch to a newborn*

Dogs who are used to being touched associate touch with comfort and nurturing. During traumatic episodes, such as automobile accidents, sports injuries and emotionally charged social interactions (dogfights) they are more likely to allow their owner/handler to be close enough to help.

We know that massage changes attitude; it changes thoughts. Thought changes brain chemistry. Brain chemistry affects health. Consider the examples of people with multiple personalities. One moment they may present with diabetes or migraine headaches, a limp or a contracted hand, all physically measurable and documentable. The next moment they may be healthy or have an entirely different set of symptoms.

The only variable was their subconscious thoughts. Subconscious thoughts create our-and our dogs' realities. We are what we think. Besides the obvious benefits of a medical massage, when dogs experience the trauma of surgery or accidents, PetMassageTM Energy Work helps them reestablish and maintain their emotional balance, their wellness.

"Pearl, my dog, becomes extremely nervous at the sound of fireworks. This past Fourth of July was especially bad, with kids in the neighborhood setting off firecrackers for several nights before the Fourth. I didn't want to medicate my dog. Even if I were going to, it would be too late after the anxiety begins. I decided to use massage techniques I learned in the workshop to try to help.

After about 15 minutes of having massaged her-the whole dog, she was able to relax and spent the rest of that night calm. The next night, when the dog began to pant and pace, I gave here another massage. Once again, she relaxed and slept the rest of the night.

The 3$^{rd}$ night was the Fourth of July. As expected, Pearl started panting and pacing again. The difference was she got up on the couch where she had been massaged the previous two nights; took a deep breath, sighed, stretched out and went to sleep." -Barb H., Toledo. OH

Pearl, the Bernese Mountain dog, learned to cope with her anxiety due to loud noises. This is a beautiful example PetMassage impacting behavior.

### Exercise 7
### Breathing

Sit quietly with your dog. Place both hands on his body, one on his croup, the other either under the neck or over the withers. Observe your breath. Focus on your inhalation through your nose and gentle exhalation through your mouth.

Feel your abdomen rise as your lungs inflate. Feel it flatten as they deflate. Allow the tip of your tongue to gently touch your upper palate just behind your front teeth.

Observe your tongue and its connection as you continue breathing. Feel the softening of the muscles in your tongue, your face, your neck, your shoulders, chest, arms and hands as you breathe.

Feel the gentle quietness as it flows out from your chest (heart), moves down your arms and hands and connects with your dog. How does this feel? How does your dog respond? What is the quality of this moment?

Chapter 8
Bonding and Confidence

PetMassage$_{TM}$ brings attention to your bodies -both yours and your dog's. Each massage session gives you information to develop and maintain a consistent assessment. You can keep track of the quality of his overall well being, his healthfulness, and any aberrations from his norm. PetMassage$_{TM,}$ on a consistent, daily or weekly schedule will help you to become your dog's first line of defense against disease and discomfort. As your awareness becomes more enhanced, you'll be more likely to detect any changes in his body. It will also draw your dog's attention to each part of his body so that he can assess his own body and quality of life at various depths and levels.

Early detection and early action is a powerful aid in treating any disease. Learning PetMassage$_{TM}$ is incredibly empowering, especially for new pet owners. If, while working with your dog you detect anything that doesn't seem quite right, even if you can't clearly describe it, consult your vet. PetMassage$_{TM}$ was created to assist and complement veterinary care.

---

Empowering for new pet owners

---

❑ **Empowers owners to work with their pets...**
As owners become more comfortable touching their dogs, they give themselves permission to become more aware. As their skills develop they respond to their dogs' communication styles more effectively. They don't just feel empowered; they *are* more empowered, more capable. They are actively and purposefully helping their dogs create and maintain a better quality of life.

❑ **Energizing your dog's mind...**
Your dog follows on the inside where he feels touch on the outside. Where your hand goes, attention knows. Focus his attention on following the movement of your hands. During the PetMassage<sub>TM</sub> session, your dogs get quite a mental workout.

The effects of your touch do not stop when the session is completed. They are long lasting, continuing to affect your dogs as they integrate their new physical and emotional rewiring into their lives.

> Where your hand goes,
> attention knows.

> Where attention goes,
> your intention flows.

Practicing PetMassage<sub>TM</sub> also energizes *our* minds. Developing the skills of PetMassage<sub>TM</sub> increases *our* awareness and sensitivity. Our hands become more sensitive to the tiniest nuances of response to our touch. We become more observant of the messages of body language. Our hearts and haras become more open to movements of the energy within our dogs' and our bodies. Our spirits become open and aware of the spirits within those around us. As we become more aware and responsive to inter-species nonverbal communication, we become more observant and sensitive to everything and everybody (intra-species) around us.

### Enhances bonding, builds confidence of both the dog *and* the person giving massage...

Dogs are so connected to their owners that they often take on their owners' fears and pathologies. You may remember Verdell, the little Brussels griffon in the movie "As Good As It Gets." Hopping over the cracks in the pavement to be like Jack Nicholson's character. As both dog and owner become more comfortable with the PetMassage_TM process, both benefit from the healing powers of touch and emotional nurturing. Bonding is strengthened. Each feels secure relying on the support of the other as they move through their activities of daily living. PetMassage_TM supports your dog's *intention* to become the whole perfect dog that is his potential. His intention is to support the perfect you that is *your* potential.

### Your sessions become a meditation time for both dog and therapist...

Massage has a direct effect on your dog's neurological systems. Increasing circulation on and along the spine opens the pathways for the cerebral spinal fluid to flow. Of the two aspects of the nervous system, the sympathetic and parasympathetic, the para-sympathetic is the one that is accessed through massage. The parasympathetic is the regenerative mode. It is the one dogs access when they go into a meditative state. Dogs may fall over in a daze, go unconscious or fall into a deep slumber. When this happens wait a few minutes to allow them to work through whatever they are dreaming about and then gently awaken them, giving them time to reorient themselves to where they are and whom they are with.

Once your dog relaxes and enters this level of consciousness you won't want to disrupt his flow.

Meditation is about being, not about doing. Sometimes, allow your hands to be quiet. They don't always have to be busy, constantly moving, groping and kneading, while giving a massage. Often the most powerful events of the PetMassage$_{TM}$ session occur when you allow yourself to just *be* with your dog in quiet stillness. Observe your breath as you gently inhale and exhale. Observe any changes in your dog's demeanor.

> Meditation is not about doing, it's about being.

We all have a tendency, while sitting or standing quietly with our dogs, for our fingers to go on autopilot, scratching and tickling our dog's coat. Project yourself into your dog's body. Feel what he is feeling. Imagine how distracting scratching and tickling would be during your session while you are trying to quiet your mind to feel your body's responses to touch.

**PetMassage$_{TM}$ gives to dogs something they can't do for themselves...**
which is measured, controlled touch. Dogs are perfectly capable of scratching their own itches. They can roll back and forth on their spines, nibble on their irritations, and lick themselves. They can twist and stretch and do all sorts of contortions. What they cannot do is maintain a measured amount of pressure on or above a given spot and hold it until a change in the tissue or energetic flow occurs. This is how we can help. We come to the table providing intuitive skills enhanced with knowledge, external attention and inner intention and purpose. We're here to bring the dog's attention to areas of his body and to help effect the healing that is more likely to occur in a rebalanced environment.

PetMassage™
- Comforts tired muscles and relieves pain
- Increases circulation to areas
- Strengthens the body by stimulating muscles
- Maintains and restores flexibility
- Alleviates pain with increased blood flow
- Energizes the mind, brings attention to the area
- Empowers owners to work with their pets
- Empowers pets to work with their owners

### Exercise 8
### Walking meditation

Start by sitting quietly outside.

Center and ground yourself by observing your breathing.

Stand. Place your feet shoulder width apart, softening your knees slightly and keeping your back vertical and your head up. Gently tilt your pelvis, tucking your sacrum under. Center your weight between your feet. Feel yourself set and balanced for a few minutes. Walk in a centered meditative manner (Exercise 4) to the closest tree and place your hands on it. Feel how solid it is.

How big around is it?

What is the color and texture of its bark?

What is the aroma of the bark?

Look up to see how high the uppermost branches rise from the ground. Sense the depth and breadth of the root system as it burrows deep underground.

Breathe with the tree.

# Unit 3
# Language

Chapter 9
Language Defining Culture, Verbal

Roger Caras wrote, "In the language of massage-body language, touch, is always understood." He was referring to the nonverbal body language. We speak volumes with our actions. And our actions are the results of our unconscious intentions. Much of PetMassage_TM is
maintaining, or not getting in the way of creating a connection with dogs. Dogs have no difficulty reading our cues, even the ones we try to hide. They can tell when our eyes dilate or the meanings of the acidity or saltiness in our perspiration. They readily offer their true purpose and intention in their body language. We need to learn to read and respond to the subtle cues that our dog's body gives us.

Roger Caras was a naturalist and television personality. His many books on animal behavior, often focus on dogs. You may remember his voice on television describing the various breeds at the Westminster Kennel Club Show. I recommend the hilarious and insightful classic, *A Dog Is Listening*, is an absolute must-read. --JR

You already know the significance of obvious body language. Their messages are clear when you see the heads or ears at certain levels or the curled up snarling attitude of the lips showing all those pretty white teeth. More important than these gross movements in body reading, are the subtle changes in the sheen of the coat, the gentle quiet expansions and contractions of skin and the internal elements deep within the muscles and joints. These are the signals we read with PetMassage_TM.

There is another way besides body language to communicate. There are words. We need to learn to communicate with other people as well.

Words are important. By understanding the language we will learn the *culture* of PetMassage_TM. In this new/old profession of PetMassage_TM, it is imperative to use the correct terminology. After all, unless we are focusing directly on music, colors or shapes, we bipeds (humans, not chickens) think in words. Even then, for us to be able to communicate our experience to someone else or to describe it to ourselves, we need words. Words define a culture, that is, a culture is defined by the words in its vocabulary. Attorneys have one language, physicians another. Artists, musicians, carpenters, farmers, scientists, and computer specialists, each have a specific language that allows members of their group to express what they need to say and be understood.

This language also sets each profession apart, making it unique; giving it specificity and credibility.

The language of PetMassage_TM draws from several cultures. It combines words and concepts from Western Medical Massage, Traditional Asian Medicine, Ayurveda theory, Native American, African and European folk traditions, Bioenergetics, Human/dog trans-cultural and trans-species communication. PetMassage_TM as a culture is just developing. In addition to the above, its language blends these convergent disciplines:

Massage therapy
Occupational therapy
Aqua- or hydrotherapy
Animal anatomy
Physiology
Western Veterinary terminology
Rebirthing/Conscious Connected Breathing
Martial arts

Oriental and Eastern Indian philosophy
Dog Training
Animal behavior
Human psychology
Animal communication
Parapsychology

We are creating a new PetMassage$_{TM}$ culture. The "culture" is defined by the words we use. Please use the correct terms, such as, *stifle* instead of *knee*, *hock* instead of *rear ankle*, and effleurage instead of light stroking. This will help create the credibility that we need for our profession to grow and flourish. The future of PetMassage$_{TM}$ as a profession is HUGE. And, for it to grow it must be nurtured and supported through accurate language usage.

Please invest a few minutes to look at the glossary. Look down the list of words to see if there are any you don't already know. As you read them, allow your mind to be guided into the rhythms of their combined impression. This is the cultural/verbal imprint of PetMassage$_{TM}$.

We will be using very few Latin words in this text, so there's no need to get nervous. When we do, we'll make sure you understand why. Latin terms usually describe

1)  the shape of something
2)  its direction
3)  its action (what it does)
4)  its location (where it is).

Knowing a few basic Latin prefixes and suffixes and a few "root" terms will help, too. The following chart has terms that are important to know.

## Coming to Terms with Your Dog:
Contours and Landmarks of the Dog

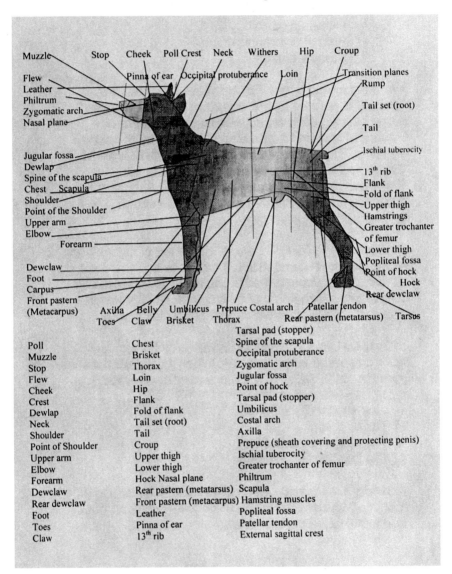

| | | |
|---|---|---|
| Poll | Chest | Spine of the scapula |
| Muzzle | Brisket | Occipital protuberance |
| Stop | Thorax | Zygomatic arch |
| Flew | Loin | Jugular fossa |
| Cheek | Hip | Point of hock |
| Crest | Flank | Tarsal pad (stopper) |
| Dewlap | Fold of flank | Umbilicus |
| Neck | Tail set (root) | Costal arch |
| Shoulder | Tail | Axilla |
| Point of Shoulder | Croup | Prepuce (sheath covering and protecting penis) |
| Upper arm | Upper thigh | Ischial tuberocity |
| Elbow | Lower thigh | Greater trochanter of femur |
| Forearm | Hock Nasal plane | Philtrum |
| Dewclaw | Rear pastern (metatarsus) | Scapula |
| Rear dewclaw | Front pastern (metacarpus) | Hamstring muscles |
| Foot | Leather | Popliteal fossa |
| Toes | Pinna of ear | Patellar tendon |
| Claw | 13th rib | External sagittal crest |

**Exercise 9**
**Review Glossary and Appendix**

Please take a few minutes to review the chart in this chapter, the glossary and the Appendix in the back of this text.

We are creating a new language. Here's an opportunity to make up a word and give it any appropriate meaning you like. Did you have a favorite made-up word in your childhood? Even then, you knew in your heart you would be part of the creation of a new culture.

Chapter 10
Language, Nonverbal

It is estimated that the largest number of specific words that dogs can understand is 250. Of these most of what is understood is because of inflection or other visual and subliminal signals that are sent with the words. Give the "down" command in a firm voice and then whisper a lilting "down" with your eyes directed toward the ceiling and see the difference in response.

**Nonverbal communication, whether human to dog, dog to dog or dog to human** has to be clear and consistent. Dogs are constantly scrutinizing our body signals. A keen sense of sight is just one of the highly efficient faculties they use to perceive their surroundings. We know that dogs are not color blind. They see colors, but just not as vibrantly as do humans. Their images are more in the pastel tones with more clarity toward the red end of the spectrum. Their vision is similar to our night, or moon vision, in which we see mostly in black and white with a few pastel overtones. Since color is not as important to them, dogs react more to movement. Again, it's similar to our night vision. This is why the language of body movements is so important.

Dogs are well aware that we are not dogs. They understand each other and react accordingly with rational consistency. And, since they do respond instinctually to the visual stimuli of body language that mimics their own, it is necessary to know some of the patterns that dogs see and interpret. We've seen that movement gets their attention. Stillness is more difficult for them to get their paws around. Dogs have short attention spans, and live in the "present." They must have a continuous stimulus or their focus will get distracted and redirected to another stimulus. When any stimulus is sensed, attention is drawn to it. If it stops, attention is befuddled and will be drawn to the next movement. This is why long sit-stays are so difficult for dogs to master. Communication, after all, is not just one sending a message and the other receiving it.

It is the correct interpretation of the received messages. If we can understand how our messages (body language) are interpreted, it will make our conversations with our dogs clearer and simpler. Although dogs are very forgiving, and will usually go with the flow, they interpret things in simple terms and in extremes.

Dogs, like most animals, react to pain, comfort and pleasure and the anticipation of pain, comfort and pleasure.

Anticipation of pain is fear. Anticipation of comfort is hopefulness and happiness. In between these two extremes is confusion. Confusion wavers between pleasure and fear. When you come home and your dogs wag their tails, they are not so much indicating that they are happy to see you, although they surely are. They are showing confusion about whether you are staying or you are leaving again. Are you here? Are you there? Are you staying? Are you going? Wag, wag, wag.

Dogs crave environmental constancy and routine. They are happiest when they know exactly what they are doing, where they are going and what is expected of them.

When dogs interact with each other they are initially seeking to know their position in the pack. This is to know who they are and what is expected of them. They start with eye contact. Once that is established and whatever information they can get is understood, they use body language

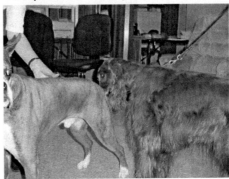

*Getting to know you.*

to indicate that they will either comply with what they've interpreted or will challenge for position. If they aren't sure whether they should mount an all-out challenge, they walk around to access each other's anal glands for information about gender, cycle, age, health, dominance, submissiveness, etc.

In the neighborhood where I walk my boxer, every time we passed one particular house, the large dog who was chained up in the side yard would bark and lunge at us ferociously. The first couple of times, Oskar would stop and stand very still, with his head pointed straight ahead, but not looking directly at the other dog. His body was angled to the side. His head was held high; his chin parallel with the ground. His eyes were opened wide. His nostrils flared and twitched taking in the smells. He held his mouth slightly open, mouth breathing. His ears were held erect and occasionally twitched to assess his surroundings. His tail was held straight up, with no lateral movement.

Oskar's stance was up on his toes, with his front paws rotated slightly to the inside, his elbows bowed slightly out to the sides. His pectoral muscles and his chest were tight and enlarged as were the muscles in the sides of his neck.

The hair on his back from withers to croup stood upright. His pasterns were behind his body, perfectly vertical. He looked imposing and larger than usual.

When we humans find ourselves in flight or fight situations, we have similar (except for the tail) instinctual physiological behaviors. Our eyes dilate and open wide, to take in as much visual information as possible. Our mouths open slightly and our breath rate changes. Our noses become engorged with blood and appear slightly bulbous to take in more olfactory information. The lips and the backs of our necks are two of the most sensitive parts of our bodies; our lips also engorge with blood, enlarging them, the hairs on the back of our neck stand up and the little erector pili muscles in our skin are stimulated to create goose bumps on our skin. All these behaviors help to give us greater skin surface area and more acute senses in order to gather as much information about our surroundings as possible.

Mimicking some of Oskar's behaviors will help us understand what he was experiencing. The first behavior we described was eye contact. When dogs look into each other's eyes, they are seeking to find out which of them is dominant. If you lock eyes with a dog, make sure that you are the one who controls the interaction. After you have established contact, you break the connection by looking up and away. This indicates dominance. Looking down and to the side indicates your submissiveness.

While giving massage or energy work, do not look into the eyes of your dog. Your dog's attention will be pulled outward to focus

> They see your eyes.

on the level of his pack status, rather than inward, where he needs to go to for his session.

Dogs need to see your eyes to know your intentions. They need to know when and why you are looking at them. If you are wearing sunglasses can they see your eyes at all?

> Dogs see your face.

They see your face. Are your eyes laughing, wide open or hard? Are the edges of your mouth turned up into a smile or have your jaw muscles tightened, pulling your lips into a scowl.

They see your posture. Do you stand straight and move with confidence and surety? Are your

> Dogs see your posture.

shoulders back and are your chest and head up? Think about what can be read into your posture.

Recall how Oskar stood straight and erect, making himself as large as he could. This power stance also imparts a large powerful aura or energetic space. Your posture is read as well.

Dogs read your health, your experience, your

> Approach, from the side.

comfort and your mood in the way you hold your body as you stand, sit, and move about.

When you first encounter a new dog, remember the boxer's stance: he stood

> Be aware of inadvertent dominance gestures.

angling his body off to one side, not looking directly at the other dog. He wanted to give the other dog an escape route if he needed one. Your dog needn't feel cornered either. Approach from the side, angle your body toward the side, and do not look directly at him/her.

Be aware if you are sending dominance signals when reaching out to touch him for the first time. You'll want to establish your dominance, but do it in the species-appropriate manner and order. You may not know this dog or what kind of emotional baggage he is bringing to the table. So, start by respecting his space and emotional vulnerability. Mentally, ask his per-mission to enter his space.

> Respect space and emotional vulnerability.

When a dog wants to show his dominance over another, he will stand over the other dog. If the other dog refuses to acknowledge his dominance, he will place his head or paw over the other's withers. If he still doesn't receive the respect he is looking for, he will press his head, paw, or shoulder down onto the others' withers, forcing the other down to the ground. The interaction is not complete until the submissive dog is lying quietly on his back under the dominant dog.

Approaching from the side, reach forward with the back of your paw (hand). The raised underside of the paw, your palm, indicates dominance or a threat, the back, submissiveness. Dogs have to use the underside, or ventral aspect of their paws to push down on the withers.

So, from the side, reach with the back of your paw (hand) and gently stroke his chest, underside of the muzzle and the side of his head, under his ears. Then, as you gain the dog's acceptance, gradually turn your hand over to stroke and scratch the top of his head behind his ears.

> Be aware of your breathing.

Be aware of your breathing. Dogs can tell if you are nervous, and your confidence level, by your breathing patterns. If you are holding your breath, the dog recognizes this is an unnatural pattern and will be uneasy in your presence. Your uneasiness will encourage his unwillingness to participate in the massage session or much worse, if he is a dominant dog and senses your fear.

*Minty fresh breath She must be okay!*

Many trainers maintain that if they keep a peppermint lozenge in their mouth, they will be able to trick the dogs into not being able to sense their apprehension. Dogs deserve more credit than this. Think how difficult it would be to try to deceive a border patrol dog sniffing for concealed contraband drugs mixed in with other fragrances. It's doubtful that if smugglers would just toss in a Lifesaver they'd be home free! Dogs are aware of your breathing patterns and the scent of your breath. Breathe, relax, and find your inner confidence.

There's no need for tricks or deception; they wouldn't work anyway. PetMassage$_{TM}$ and all energy work are based on trust, acceptance and sharing. Your communication is enhanced when you know how you are seen through your dog's eyes. As your own body awareness becomes more developed, your signals will be clearer and more controlled. With enhanced observation and experience you will soon be able to understand your own body language and your dog's language, too.

**We communicate by scent...**
Dogs have an incredibly keen sense of smell. This is
not news. Dogs not only are aware of such synthetic
fragrances as colognes, perfumes and deodorants;
they can also tell what you had for lunch, and even
how efficiently you are digesting it. They sense subtle
variations in the chemistry of your sweat. This is how
they know when their owners are soon to have
seizures or heart attacks. Dogs can smell fear. They
can also *taste* fear, yours and their own. Dogs are
hardwired to look for imbalances (movement), or
diseases in your breath and in your skin.

They use this information to confirm their level of
safety and security as well as their position in their
social order. This information is for protection and,
when they need to hunt, for tracking and killing of prey.

Your confidence, your experience, your wellness, your
openness and presence are all there in the scents you
exude and bring with you.

**Your presence and your intention...**communicate
volumes. On a very basic and intuitive level, dogs
understand why you are there and what you can offer
them. They know when your presence supports and
enhances their lives. They can also tell when someone
might be a threat, or simply not making a
complementary energetic connection.

Whenever one particular woman in our office building
pulls her car up in front of our school, however many
dogs we have inside become agitated. She never
enters the classroom nor looks in the windows. None
of the dogs have previously met her. Yet, they jump
about in their crates, pawing at the metal grids of the
doors or rush at the door, barking at her. They
somehow sense her lack of connection. Her presence
alone provokes this extreme reaction.

**We project *our thoughts*.**
Our moods are reflected in our posture. If your body
language projects a closed mind, why would any dog
bother attempting to connect? They are frustrated

enough attempting to communicate with us using their consistent signals of body language even when we are being open and focused! If no one's home, there is no one available to receive signals.

There was a great Gary Larson (The Far Side) cartoon that shows in the first frame a dog with the caption "Bark, bark, bark, bark, bark.' The second frame shows the same picture with the translation, "Hey, hey, hey, hey, hey."

Dogs do not have a large vocabulary. They do not need to communicate in words; instead, they send thought images with strong emotional overtones.

Here are some experiences of how dogs can clearly project and receive images.

**Oskar's toy**

Across the parking lot from our PetMassage™ Institute is an emergency medic. Ambulances pull in and out of their garage several times a day. For the first couple of weeks we were in this location, every time one of the ambulances would pull out of the garage, Oskar, our boxer, would rush to the large front window and bark frantically. I couldn't figure out why he was so agitated.

One of our students, who is an excellent animal communicator observed Oskar and started laughing. She pointed to the fuzzy red dice hanging from the rear view mirror of one of the vehicles and told me that Oskar thinks those are *his* toys. She knelt down and silently told him that they weren't his and that he needn't get upset.

His behavior immediately changed. From that moment, he paid no more attention to the ambulances.

## Doberman's back porch

Several years ago, while demonstrating PetMassage~TM~ at a dog show in Michigan, a young woman brought her 90 pound Doberman to our booth and hauled him up onto the massage table. I asked her permission to work on her dog and then asked the dog for his. I closed my eyes and allowed my hands to be directed to the parts of his body that needed touch the most.

I soon became aware that I was observing an image of the back entrance of a house. I saw gray-painted cement steps; the top slab landing had a front corner chipped off, that had been painted over. There was a thick brown rough doormat in front of the yellow half step up into the doorway. The door was painted red; the door surround was painted yellow. To my amazement, I realized that I was looking *up* at the worn brass doorknob. I asked her if this sounded familiar.

Author demonstrates PetMassage~TM~ at Michigan UKC Show

Her eyes opened wide as she exclaimed that this was her back stoop, right down to the chipped cement. I had never experienced this clear of a psychic image while working with dogs before. I got all goose-bumpy at the total weirdness of this experience when the next impression I had really put me back on my heels. I said, "I believe your dog is telling me that when the porch is wet, it is slippery. He doesn't like to wait out there when it's wet."

"It *is* slippery when it's wet," she said. "I didn't think he minded. I'll have to watch him closer."

Where did this thought-image come from? The day was warm and sunny with a light breeze. Somehow, her dog had the need and the ability to transmit this stored memory. He shared it with me so something could be done about his concern about his slippery back steps. He had projected the image and the emotion that was connected to it. So, this is what the animal communicator sees and knows!

**Dogs sense of sense**

What *do* dogs perceive? They can detect earthquakes and thunder-storms before they happen. They can track skiers buried under several feet of snow. They help their owners to find safe places prior to heart attacks, seizures and migraines. They can smell subtle fluctuations in the composition of our sweat. They can detect variations and fluctuations in normal body heat. Dogs sense subtle changes in their humans' body language such as how often you blink or how dilated your pupils are. In addition to seeing all the things that we can see, they are aware of *qualities* of the layers of energy moving through and around the body. This is how they can recognize us from a hundred yards away. They see us, as we are, bright, shining, vibrational beings.

> Barking dogs never bite, while barking.

**Your responsiveness to your dog's body...**

When you are in the dog's presence, sharing your space with his, with your energetic body connecting with his, sense the interactions and resilience of both your auric bodies. When you assess your dog's body using compression or gentle kneading, sense the resilience of the tissues. Feel *your* responses to his tiny movements released through his positional release (Chapter 13), his ruffling and unruffling (Chapter 35), and healing touch (Chapter 35).

Your dog's reactions to your touch can be subtle, some-times not so subtle. Sometimes, you sense nothing. Sometimes you can feel huge movements within the joints of the dog. Most likely, you'll feel the tiny movements somewhere between these extremes. Your ability to feel what is going on within and around the dog will increase with experience.

Often, we sense the unwinding of releases by having in our mind's eyes, the sensation of floating, whirling or twisting. It is often easier to experience this feeling with extraneous distractions removed. With closed eyes, and your still hands placed on your dog, imagine your entire body moving with the motions you perceive under your hands. First the flow may go in one direction. Then, it may slow, stops, and reverse itself. Follow it, until the movement comes to a place of peace and comfort and stops. This is the balance that your dog's body is seeking.

You might observe other sensations in your body that might reflect what's happening within your dog. Your palms may get warm and tingly. You may yawn, burp, pass gas or sneeze. Your nose or other area of your skin may itch. Your tummy may gurgle; you may feel fatigue, cramping, stiffness, nausea or a headache. You may get the feeling of acute awareness. You may sense that spirit guides are at your side, assisting you. You may feel your heart race. You may sense a feeling of wondrous balance. You may feel absolute calm.

You will soon realize how intricately connected you and your dog have become. Your moving with his body will help him unwind. What is being unwound? Memories and their traumas are tightly bound up in the muscles, fascia and other parts of the body. They are opening up to be released. Opening the pathways in your dog's body puts him in the operating mode of healing and regeneration. In the language of touch, body language is always understood.

**Signs of acceptance or refusal to participate in the massage session...**

The signs of acceptance or refusal can be big and obvious but usually they are very subtle. Weight shift toward you usually indicates acceptance, away, indicates distancing and avoidance. These are easy to see. You will also notice slight changes in the sheen in the coat, reflecting an auric shift of acceptance.

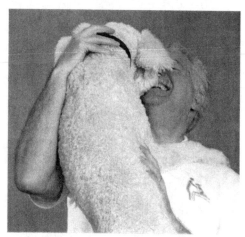

*Sometimes Jocko and Jonathan would rather play.*

The hair on his topline from neck to croup is constantly shifting; the movement moving with the dog's breathing and his/her moment-to-moment assessment of safety and sense of control.

- Weight shift towards you indicates acceptance
- Weight shift away, indicates distancing
- Softening of the coat along the topline indicates no threat to pack status and acceptance of touch
- A shift in the light in the eyes indicates you have the dog's attention
- Quick eye contact: all you need to see is a quick glance and acknowledgement that you are sharing his space

> Neither you nor the observers ought to make eye contact with the dog. Keep the dog's attention focused and moving within.

While giving massage make sure that neither you nor the observers make eye contact with your dog/client. Your dog will instinctually and intellectually go into a control pack-level mode. We need to keep your dog's

attention focused and moving within. You can look *at* the eyes; but do not be drawn into them.

**Canine Body Language…**
Some of the dominance movements that dogs demonstrate toward humans include flattened or erect attitude of the ears. erect or tense wagging

*Look into my eyes -I own you*  tail,.

face pointing directly at you, hair on neck and back raised, up on toes, eye contact, and, let's not forget humping. Of course lips curled up into a snarl and bearing of fangs are signs that are pretty hard to misinterpret. Some submissive movements are compressing the tail tightly against rump or between legs, cowering, making a chewing motion with the mouth and rolling onto his/her back. Oh, and don't forget piddling upon confrontation.

*Oskar pays no attention to puppy*

There are specific movements, which dogs understand that indicate dominance or submissiveness. Pack hierarchy establishes and maintains order and civility within the group. The amount of dominance or submissiveness shown indicates each dog's level in his pack or social order. This is very important for dogs. Not every dog needs to aspire to the top level. Just knowing his/her place is sufficient to maintain peace. Just as small children play fight and role-play to learn adult skills, puppies also learn from play fighting and testing what behavior is acceptable and appropriate.

Humping indicates dominance, or intent for dominance. It could also show confidence. It could also express "pack drive." Level of ears indicates level of interest. The level of the tail indicates how visible (present) the dog wants to be. It also indicates confidence and dominance, or shyness and submission.

Attitude or level of the head carriage indicates pack status. Also the level of the tail is an indicator of pack status.

> When my instructor (Oskar, the boxer) and I used to walk to a nearby park, there was a dog at the corner of the street who would lunge at the fence whenever we would walk by. Even when he wasn't out, the hair on Oskar's back would rise as we approached the house and quickly flatten as soon as we were past.
>
> Oskar wouldn't appear to show any other reaction. He didn't look for the dog. He didn't alter his gait. He didn't move from one side of the sidewalk to the other. I could monitor his anxiety level by simply watching the movement of his coat. Occasionally he would pee on the tree in front of the fence to mark his scent as a reminder of his presence to the other dog.

Dog's licking your mouth indicates submissiveness. We would like to believe that this means they love us and are kissing us; but the instinctual behavior of puppies tells us otherwise. The most appropriate puppy chow is partially digested food. When puppies are hungry, they will lick their mother's mouth, stimulating the regurgitation reflex.

So, if the next time your dog licks your mouth, show them you care. Give them what they really want.

The hackles (hairs on the back of the neck) are raised to show the level of concern. When dogs are threatened, they are not always raised all the way.

There are degrees that would indicate to us and to other dogs their level of apprehension.

Dogs' toes, ankles and elbows speak volumes. When a dog is demonstrating boldness, no matter what size dog, he/she will rise up on their toes, angle their feet a little more toward the inside pushing their elbows outward. This puts their legs in a better position for the fast movements needed for fighting or fleeing.

Chewing motions with the mouth and licking their lips indicate submission, willingness to learn, and to do whatever it takes to join up with the pack. Showing their canines is certainly a threatening signal, one hard to miss.

Turning to the side, sitting down and/or yawning are also signals that dogs are responding to situations that are stressful. These behaviors are body language saying they would like to disassociate themselves from the activity. Turid Rugaas has written some excellent papers on calming signals that dogs use to avoid violence. They use them with other dogs and, since this is their primary language, they look for these signals from people, too.

When Oskar has had enough of the young Jocko's play, he sits down and turns his back on the younger dog. Jocko understands. He immediately stops and looks for someone else in the family to badger. When Oskar wants to initiate play, he will walk away, but look back with his head cocked and his ears down. Jocko doesn't need to be asked twice. He drops his chew-toy and pounces; play biting Oskar's back legs. The match is on again.

Dog culture… prevents dogs from willingly displaying their pain and weakness. It indicates vulnerability. The pack responds and survives by destroying the weakest links. Vulnerability in the wild weakens the integrity of the pack. One of our clients was an elderly Springer Spaniel who was suffering from a seizure disorder. The first time I saw him he presented with scars and huge swaths of his coat missing. He would have grand mal seizures at home, fall unconscious and be attacked by the other 3 dogs in the house. His pack

had been living harmoniously with him for many years until he showed his weakness. He'd had to be rescued and treated several times for severe bite wounds and mauling.

*Dogs can be clever manipulators.*

It was the law of the pack.

Recent studies with hidden videos have shown that when dogs believe they are alone, they display the symptoms of pain and discomfort i.e., shallow breathing, limping, wincing, groaning and whining with movement. The same dogs, when in the presence of people or other dogs put on a brave façade, appearing confident, fully mobile and in good spirits. Stoicism is a necessity in their culture for survival.

On the other hand, we all know dogs can be clever manipulators. Attention and sympathy treats are good reasons for them to limp, whine or pretend that they are at death's door.

## Chapter 10
## Pushing a tree

Start by sitting quietly outside. Observe your breathing to center and ground yourself. Stand, and place your feet shoulder width apart, bending your knees slightly and keeping your back vertical and your head up. Gently tilt your pelvis, tucking your sacrum under. Center your weight between your feet. Feel yourself set and balanced for a few minutes. Walk in a centered meditative manner to a mature tree and place your hands on it. Feel how solid it is. How big around is it? What is the color and texture of its bark? What is the aroma of the bark? Look up to see how high the uppermost branches rise into the sky. Sense the depth and breadth of the root system as it burrows deep underground.

Push the tree and feel if it moves. The wind can cause trees to sway and bend. Sense the entire length of the tree from the bottom of the roots to the top of its branches. Visualize the pulse of light as it moves from the roots to the tops of the branches and back down. Up and down the light flows through your hands. Feel the life force energy as it moves through the tree.

# Unit 4
# Awareness and Energy

## Chapter 11
## Increasing Sensory Awareness

In our workshops we practice exercises to increase our sensory awareness. The first of them is to closely observe a session of the instructor giving and a dog receiving a basic full body PetMassage<sub>TM</sub> session.

We discuss our thoughts, feelings and awareness'.
We *see* the massage, *hear* the massage, *feel* the massage and *be*come aware of many of the nuances that we might have missed before. We learn to closely observe the dog to catch tiny changes in the eyes, tail, ears, coat and respiratory rate. We

*Barb H. with her Berner*

note the amount of perspiration by the paw prints before, during and after the massage. These are just the gross, most obvious forms of non-verbal communication.

*See* the massage: Observe the dog's movements, and demeanor before, during and after the massage, his nonverbal communication. How willing is he or she to participate? What are the body language signals? How does your dog react to your presence? How does he respond to your touch? Is there any difference in his gait after the session?

*Hear* the massage: Discover the many types of verbal animal communication. Listen for animal breathing, panting and throat sounds. Listen to your own thoughts and feelings. Sometimes your own voices in your head are so loud, they drown out any other information that's trying to get through. When you quiet them, you can become more open to any images and suggestions our dogs might be sending.

*Feel* the massage: Your physical tools are your hands. Use your whole hand. Use the front, sides and back, fingertips, thumb, knuckles, heel and wrist. For greatest control and sensitivity, keep your wrists, finger joints and muscles supple and relaxed. Sense for qualities and variations in shapes and textures, such as smoothness, roughness, temperature, moisture, thickness, thinness, fullness and emptiness, flow and stagnation. You can feel values of each of these whenever you touch your dog's body. The lower part of the center of your palm (where the lines of your "life" and "heart" converge) is an area very sensitive to slight fluctuation in temperature.

In their course of animal acupressure, Amy Snow and Nancy Zidonis teach students to assess the Master Points of the Bladder Meridian, along the topline, using the base of their palms.

We not only feel the physicality of the dog. We also observe our own "feelings" during the massage process. Do you feel warm or cold, comfortable, safe, confident, or calm? Are you holding your breath? Feeling tight or out of balance? Are you straining your muscles to reach over and around the dog? Do you feel you are connecting with the dog? Are you providing for the needs of your dog? Are you focused? Are you open to the various options the dog may need for healing? Do you feel happy, on purpose, fulfilled?

*Be* the massage: Your spiritual tools are your awareness, openness to all those subtle and not so subtle cues emanating from the dog. Your awareness is your connection with dogs. Keep breathing. When you hold your breath, your Ch'i stagnates, your hands tighten and you'll lose the sensitivity in your touch. Your dog will sense any disruption in your connection with him.

---

Softening of the coat along the topline indicates no threat to pack status and acceptance of touch.

---

OBSERVATION:

Each PetMassage$_{TM}$ session begins with first observing the dog, allowing him/her to walk about and become comfortable with the environment. We note symmetry of the body.

We note the straightness or curvature of the spine and the quality of muscles running on either side of it. We notice the straightness and soundness of the legs, joints and paws.

We observe the gait at the walk and trot and the way the body is carried. Is there stiffness, lameness, lack of coordination, decreased extension in the front or rear, stumbling or partial paralysis? Is your dog double tracking or walking with his back roached? When he sits, is it square or on one hip? When he stands does he favor one side over another? We assess his mood, his comfort level as he sits, stands, turns and moves about the room.

Look for skin lesions, or matted fur. Is the coat clean and shiny? Are the nails torn or in good condition? Are the ears clean? Do they have a sour odor? Are the eyes bright and alive or dull and lifeless? Is the head held up with alertness? How does the tail hang? Is it down, out to one side, straight back, or up? Is it still or wagging? Does your dog strive to make eye contact with you? Does he slink under a table to hide?

Then when you get the dog up onto the table, place your hands on his body (or sometimes, just stand with the dog without touching). Observe your breathing. This is to center and ground y*ourself.*

Ask the dog for permission to participate in the session. You can ask the question out loud. Or, hold in your mind's eye the image of your dog receiving his PetMassage$_{TM}$ Energy session in comfort, safety and grace.

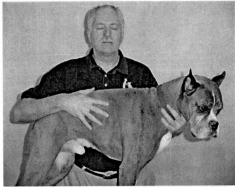

*Center*

*Ask permission*

Obtaining permission creates the bond of a contract, in which you are responsible for what happens on the outside of the body, and your dog is responsible for what goes on inside.

Dogs will accept only as much therapy as they can handle. A session that lasts longer than the dog is willing to participate lessens the impact. Your dog will become more anxious if he senses that his needs are no longer being acknowledged. This may even undo work that has been done. We can give and make information available, serve the tray, he will choose to eat. When he has stopped eating, stop the feeding.

In this course, will begin with a review of the physical massage techniques and then move on to esoteric skills.

> The PetMassage$_{TM}$ form is
> REACTIVE:
> Sensing > palpation > sensing >
> REACTING>
> palpation ...

### Exercise 11
### Opening the channel to your inner voice

Sit quietly, observing your breath. Detach yourself from the thoughts that enter your mind. Observe them but do not attach to them. Allow them to enter, briefly linger, and float away. Pay attention to the thoughts that you have never had before. Do they pertain to your dog? Are they infused with an emotion or sensation?

An important element of this exercise is not to try too hard. Allow the message to flow into your consciousness. If you have to force yourself to hear or feel, then it will be merely an extension of your imagination.

It is not always possible to read your dog's mind. Often, your receptors will be shut down. And often, your dog has no need to convey anything specific other than respect and love of your presence.

Chapter 12
Movements of PetMassage™

The specific movements used in PetMassage™ are:

**Touch**
*Touch*(ing) is contacting the dog's surface or space with no lateral movement. Place your hand on your dog's body. *Touch* your dog. Dogs perceive their bodies at many levels. You will connect to your dog at various depths using these levels of pressure:

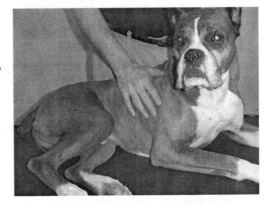

- Light
- Medium
- Firm and
- Off- body

*Oskar follows on the inside wherever Jonathan touches on the outside.*

The **Light** pressure is very light. It is about the weight of a nickel, or five grams. You will actually have to use your will and strength to hold your hand away from the body as you just caress the surface of the coat. Practice this light touch on yourself by placing a nickel on your thigh or the back of your hand. Then touch yourself with a similar amount of pressure.

**Medium** pressure is the weight of your hand resting on the body. Remember, touch has no lateral movement. Place your hand on your dog's body and allow it to rest there with no motion, neither side to side nor deeper to lighter (in and out).

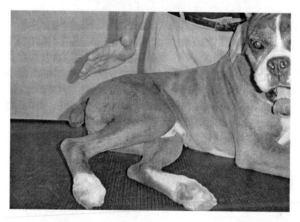 

For *Firm* pressure, press in or squeeze enough to feel the contours of the bones, muscles, tendons, ligaments, etc. beneath the skin. Press and hold. Release and repeat.

**Off- body**, hold your hand above your dog's body. You can be any distance you choose from the body, from a half-inch to several feet. Visualize a thread connecting your hand to any spot or area on his body. You are still touching – connecting to - your dog. Your awareness of each other's space is in itself a connection.

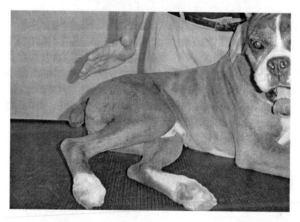

*Touch, off – body (Note Oskar's tongue. Yawning shows his awareness and participation in "aura" work.*

**Compression**
Hold your hand or fingers on one spot on your arm. Press in, hold, and release, steady in - steady out. Practice moving through the three levels of pressure. Touch *lightly*; relax your hand to rest with *medium* pressure and then press to *firm*. Hold, and slowly release back through medium and then to light. At each level, pause. At each level, feel your connection to your dog and sense his response to your touch at that depth.

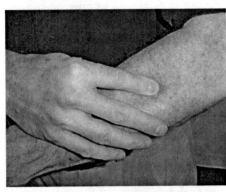

Capillary refill. When you press on your own skin, you can see the color change from flesh color to pale as you compress the blood out of the capillaries just under the surface (subcutaneous) of your skin. Release the pressure, and observe your skin color as it returns to normal. Blood returns to the area. This is an example of how easily touch and compression can affect blood circulation. This is also a way to assess hydration of the body. If it takes several seconds for the gums to return to their normal pink color, your dog is dehydrated and may need to be evaluated by your vet.

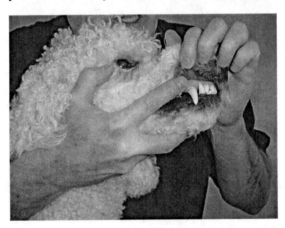

*Press and release on the gum*

*to observe capillary refill.*

Your dog follows your hands. His attention goes wherever your hand goes. He'll sense his body where your hand is lightly touching. He will feel your presence and touch in his coat, just beneath, in the connective tissue or deeper still, within his muscles, joints and bones.

His attention goes wherever your hand goes.

**Stroking ...**

is *touch* with *movement*. Again, use the pressures of Light, Medium, Firm, and off - body.

Place your hand on your dog's shoulder and allow it to move down his leg. Keep the pressure even with each stroke: light, medium, firm or off-the-body at several different distances. The stroking movement is easy and natural. In the early stages, it is the most like petting. You will soon develop an appreciation for how much you will be able to assess with this "simple" movement.

The **direction** your hands move during stroking movements is important. Strokes can have the effect of being either relaxing or stimulating. So, you can either stimulate or relax your dog by stroking in specific directions.

Movements away from the heart, with the lay of the hair are called, proximal (near) to distal (far). They *relax*.

1. Movements toward the heart move distal to proximal, and work against the grain of the hair. They are *stimulating*.

2. Movement in the direction of the flow of the meridian  (see Chapter 20), increases, or stimulates flow. Stroking against the direction of the flow of the meridian, decreases, or impedes flow.

> Direction of stroking:
> Movement with the lay of the hair is
> *relaxing.*

> Direction of stroking:
> Movement against the grain of the hair is
> *stimulating.*

> Stroking <u>in</u> the direction
> of the flow of the meridian, increases flow.

> Stroking <u>against</u> the direction
> of the flow of the meridian, decreases flow.

Let's make this a little more interesting. Each of the depths of pressure in your strokes affects a different aspect of the body. Light touch, for example, affects the lymphatics. Medium touch affects the blood flow in the skin and superficial muscles (those closest to the surface). And, deep touch affects the fascia and more internal components of your dog's body.

Light fingertip brushing, in the direction of the heart, from distal to proximal, over the 5 major lymph nodes (bilaterally) and the spleen, stimulates lymphatic drainage and supports the body's autoimmune system.

Medium depth stroking proximal to distal is relaxing, supports the arterial blood flow through the superficial muscles to the limbs and to the head. Medium stroking distal to proximal, against the lay of the hair is stimulating. It can support venous blood flow (movement back to the heart), emotionally excite your dog, or move an excited animal further into his excitement pattern, to the point where his body becomes over stimulated. His internal feedback system sends the signal for him to settle down, to a more balanced, controlled state.

Deep stroking with the grain of the hair supports the deeper movements of blood, lymph and interstitial fluids; against the lay of the hair, it impedes, or slows down the internal flows.

Work off-the body: The depths of light, medium and deep on the aura elicited through intention and visualization. Once you have located and accessed one of the energy shells around your dog's body, maintain your connection with touch. Follow the contour of the shell with stroking movements. Even working in the energetic body, the aura, your movements toward the heart are stimulating and those away from the heart are going to be relaxing. You can choose to connect with your dog's auric shell lightly, with medium pressure or deep pressure, depending on what you're intentions are and how you would like to support his life-altering experience.

**Rolling the skin AKA, skin rolling**
Skin rolling stretches the connective tissue beneath the skin. It increases blood and lymph circulation. It expands surface area to expose Ch'i receptors, or, acupoints. Grasp the coat and pull it away from the body, rolling it between your fingers and palm. Feel the skin and the connective tissue, the fascia under the skin, stretch and retract back onto the body. Visualize pulling taffy or silly putty.

Wait until you feel the skin retract before you release. This empowers the dog to control the massage. Your dog chooses when and how much manipulation of skin he is comfortable experiencing.

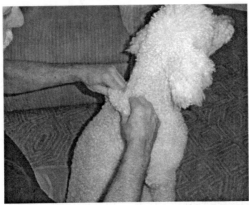

Lift skin with rolling motion of your wrists.

Allow the skin to release back onto the body.

You can skin roll all the way from the neck to the base of the tail. Remember to respect your dog's space by staying aware of the amount of flexibility and elasticity of his coat. Only pick up as much or as little of the coat as your dog is comfortable allowing you. Many older, stiffer, or those

who are not used to massage, will exhibit tenderness or tightness over their lumbar and sacral regions. The aggressiveness of your rolling can increase as they become more comfortable with their bodies and with their trust in your touch. Skin rolling is a variation of petrissage, or deep stroking.

Skin rolling is very effective over the shoulders, hips, neck, and chest as well. It enhances circulation, flexibility and perhaps most importantly, your dog's body awareness.

## Rolling and rocking

Rocking restores balance, flexibility in the spine (blood Ch'i), motility of gut (food Ch'i), and has the added benefit, as a weight bearing exercise, of increasing bone density.

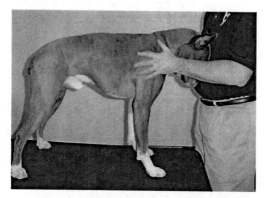

Rocking involves moving the entire body back and forth. There are four ways to Rock and Roll the body.

1.  If the dog is standing, place one hand on either side of his hips, shoulders or neck and gently shove his body to one side. As he rights himself, support his movement by pushing his body toward the other side, moving in the same direction he is moving.

As he rights himself by rocking back toward the center, continue his movement into your other hand. Create a rhythm as he moves from side to side.

*Photos on this page: Rocking side to side.*

The effects of this simple movement are dramatic. It increases circulation and lymphatic drainage. It enhances balance, muscle tone, and muscle control. Neurologically, it enhances proprioceptiveness and it even increases bone density, as your dog has to support more than twice his weight on each side as he rocks.

2. Rock your dog front to back. Grasp the base of the tail or croup in one hand and the withers or chest in the other. Push and pull developing a rocking motion, from front to back and back to front. This helps loosen up

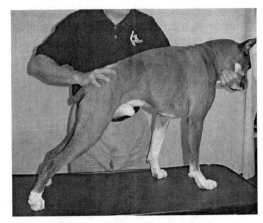

*Rocking, standing, forward and backward*

a tight neck, shoulders, hips and spine. This strengthens the hamstrings, the stifles hocks, pasterns, elbows and other joints. It also aides in digestion, coat and skin problems.

If your dog is lying on his side, push his body just far enough so that, when you let go, it rocks back to you. Continue his movement as he racks back by pulling his body to you. Once it is pulled over to you, you feel it fall back toward the center. As you slowly push and pull*, feeling for his natural rhythm and tempo. Each session will be slightly different. His rate will be influenced by who he is, how he feels and by the dynamics of your combined energy patterns.

*This has no relation, Dr. Doolittle's "pushmi-pullyus" two-headed llama.

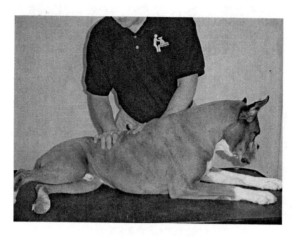

*Pushing motion*

Relaxing and comforting, pushing stimulates and rearranges the internal organs just as a good stretch does. This is especially helpful for older dogs, who have limited movement and activity and post surgery dogs, to help move the drugs through their systems.

Rocking softens the fascia and helps whole body circulation, digestion and lymphatic movement

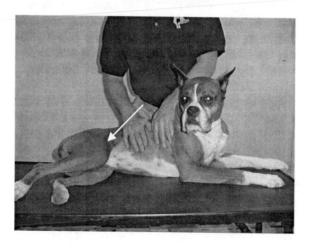

*Pulling motion*

*Rolling the shoulder*

**Rolling**

Place your hands on either side of a major joint complex such as the neck, the shoulder, elbow, or hip. Gently friction the surfaces of the area by simultaneously rubbing your palms back and forth on both sides. This warms and softens the tissues, increasing blood circulation and preparing the area for deeper work.

When the temperature in your hands begins to warm, press in with your palms while maintaining firm contact with the coat. Using the same push and pull motion, moving the coat, skin and muscles back and forth over the underlying structures within the joint complex.

This helps to soften the fascia, the connective tissue under the skin and within the muscles. It increases the blood flow through the muscles and, since the major lymph nodes are located at the major joints (Submandibular, Axillary, Prescapular, Inguinal and Popliteal, it helps move the lymphatic fluid through the body. Within the joint complexes, joint rolling increases the movement and distribution of synovial fluid and strengthens the attachment sites of tendons and ligaments.

Rocking and Rolling helps promote flexibility in the joints, muscles and fascia. It increases motility of the gut and flexibility of the spine. It enhances the flow of Cerebral spinal fluid through the spinal cord and out to the rest of the body. It supports and enhances the neural pathways from the extremities back to the brain. In other words, it supports both the Central Nervous and the Peripheral Nervous Systems. It enhances flow of energy along meridians.

**Percussion**
Percussion, or tapotement, is an integral part of PetMassage$_{TM}$ bodywork. By tapping with the fingertips, or hacking with the side of the palm, or cupping with tightly curved hands, we can stimulate the tissues and fluids in the body. All percussion is done with soft flexible wrists and, with the exception of cupping, soft, loosely held fingers. The motion is a bouncing of your hand on the body. Cupping, we will see is a great tool in our respiratory enhancement technique.

**The integration shake**
After a massage, dogs often give a full body shake, their own version of rocking and rolling. This is that fabulous shake that starts at the nose and travels all the way down the body to the tip of the tail. In the process dogs shake their legs right off the ground! We call it "the integration shake." With this movement the dog accepts and owns the new information that he acquired during his session.

Sometimes your dog will only shake as far as the shoulders, or mid-spine, or include one hip and not the other, or just up to the tail. The stopping point indicates where there is a blockage of blood circulation, joint stiffness, disease, or Ch'i, life force. Observing the integration shake, you'll be able to tell if and where more opening work may need to be done to unblock stagnation at these points.

### Exercise 12
### Rolling the dog's body

Place both hands firmly on your dog, one on one side and the other on the opposite side. With firm contact on the coat, move your hands back and forth, stretching the coat, first one way then the other in a gentle rolling motion. This warms the tissues by stretching the fascia, which increases circulation, and opens the pathways for energetic movement.

Practice this over the ribcage, the neck, each shoulder (one hand under the axilla, the other on the outside, over the deltoid) and each hip (one hand under the leg high up in the groin, the other on the outside, over the hip joint).

Move each limb only as much as your dog is comfortable moving. Allow him or her to control the amount and strength of the movement. As you move the limb to each side, remember to wait for it to respond by falling back to center. Continue the direction of its movement to the other side until you feel it has reached the limit of its full range of motion and starts to fall back toward center. Continuing with sensitivity and respect for your dog's inner awareness, this movement helps his or her body achieve peace, balance and harmony.

Chapter 13
Stretching to Follow—on

**Stretching**
In his book *Canine Massage,* Jean Pierre Hourdebaigt states "Stretching enhances energy flow by drawing out the muscles and tendons."

Stretching also enhances body awareness. During a stretch the dog takes an internal inventory of how his individual body parts are functioning. On the unconscious level - the subconscious level - the dog is readjusting and realigning his internal organs, skeletal joints and fascia to new, more comfortable positions.

This is natural "movement to a place of comfort."

> Stretching is a natural
> movement in the pursuit of
> a place of comfort.

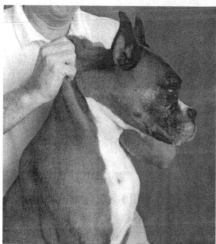

*Pull the coat straight up and hold it up until it begins its recoil. Feel the elasticity.*

**Stretching the coat**
Assisting the dog in pulling his coat away from his body is similar to skin rolling. Grasp the hide, pulling the coat straight up and hold it up until you feel the elasticity begin its recoil. Then, lower the coat back onto the body and pick up another swath of

95

coat in a different, adjoining place. This movement helps invigorate the elastin in the skin, increases blood flow through the capillaries and evens out the twists and kinks in his fascia. Skin rolling and joint rolling are both types of stretching.

### Contraindication: Stretching the limbs

It is inappropriate to grab a dog's leg and yank it. Any tugging or jerking of a dog's limbs against his/her will may cause injury and create an adversarial relationship between you. An essential skill in the practice of PetMassage$_{TM}$ is your awareness of the rate and direction of each return movement within the tissues or bones and within the joints.

### Assistive stretching to access internal wisdom

When you assist your dog in the movement of extending his limbs away from the core of his body, do so only with his full cooperation and impulsion. All movements are the dog's choice, and all movements must come from within the dog. You must acknowledge

*Warm tissues <u>before</u> any stretching*

the elements within the joints that control their movements.

NOTE:

Use compressions, frictioning, light tapping, ROM exercises to warm tissues <u>before</u> any stretching.

Before any stretching, or any manipulation, warm the tissues.

After warming the tissues with frictioning strokes, use the positional release techniques (see Chapter 13) to connect with the inner wisdom of each joint.

What wisdom is there inside a joint? The spaces between each of the elements within the joint, the bones, cartilage, ligaments, tendons, bursa, synovial fluid, etc. has individual internal awareness of its most correct and comfortable arrangements, connections, angulations and pressures. A continuous inner, wordless dialogue among the elements within each joint tells the body how, when and what to move. The elements of this conversation are part chemical, part physiological, part psychological, part genetic, part karmic, and part cosmic.

By cosmic, we are referring to that great storehouse of all cultural knowledge and wisdom that is located in what Dr. Deepak Chopra calls, the "gap." Others call it a Universal Consciousness, and still others refer to it as the Akashic Record. It is this information and awareness that is accessed through meditation. The information is all around us, within each cell of our bodies and each recess of memory held in our muscles and brain. It is the information in the "gaps" within the structures of the fascia and joints that your dog accesses when he is given the choice to move his body to a more comfortable, more balanced state.

When all parts are in balance, homeostasis is achieved. Homeostasis is balance. It is this inner wisdom that controls digestion, heart rate, hormone production and distribution, neurological functioning and everything else in his body.

When any aspect of his functioning is out of balance, we have dys-function, or disease. If the elements within the spine or joints are out of alignment, there is reduced mobility, reduced energy, reduced life force and reduced quality of life.

When parts of the body are held in fixed, unnatural and uncomfortable positions, your dog's body has somehow become disconnected with its source of internal wisdom and is using its energy to maintain unhealthy holding patterns. Placing the joint or fascia structures in relaxed, open or closed positions, his body can reconnect with Source to correct joint or tissue alignment.

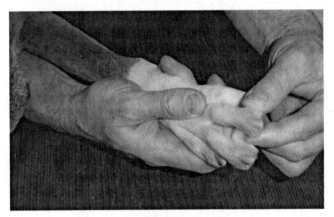

*Stretching the toe*

Focus on individual joints. Another name for joint is articulation. The amount of pressure used is minimal, just enough to sense that the space within the joint is gently extended, no more than that. It is more of a guiding than a pulling. In fact, you do not have to physically move your hands at all. Allow your intention to do the moving.

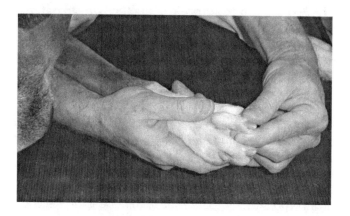

*Stretching toe to compression*

Gently grasp the limb below the joint with one hand and support above the joint with the other. Observe your first hand pull gently away from the second.

When you feel you have just about extended the joint to its full range of motion, hold it in its new position for a few moments. Feel for it to naturally contract. Release the tension and guide it toward its newly normalized position.

You can help your dog rebalance and realign each of the joints in his body: each toe, each elbow, shoulder, hip and each vertebra in the spine.

Rebalancing ~ Realigning
by the body,
for the body,
within the body

**The Expansion Response** is another way to get to the stretch. It supports the rebalancing and realignment. This is all done by the body, and for the body, and within the body. The body knows how best to balance itself. So, there is never any need to feel you have to force any of the movements.

Expansion starts with compression. Place your hands or fingers with light to medium pressure on both sides of a joint in your dog's body; such as, the carpus, or wrist area. Gently compress your hands together. Hold the position until you sense that there is an opening or unwinding starting to happen within the joint. As you support the position, note any sensation of subtle twisting or sliding.

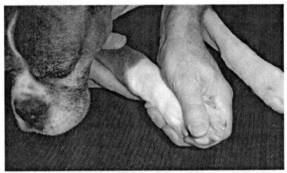

*Expansion response—*
*from compression . . to expansion (stretch)*

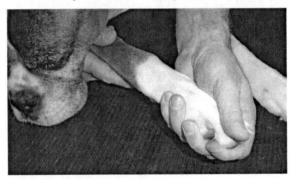

Allow your hands to move in to support these movements. Slowly release the pressure between your hands, allowing the tissues to normalize, returning back to their original position. The elements within the joints will return at slightly different angulations and tensions, having made tiny skeletal adjustments. From the compressed position, the joint seeks its place of comfort in expanding.

This is called *Positional Release*. The joint is placed in a supported position and allowed to unwind, or release, following its internal knowing, to a more comfortable situation. The journey that the limb or body part makes en route is called *exploration of movement*.

Note that you are not the one making any of the adjustments. You are observing and supporting the dog's intuitive responses.

> The dog determines all movements.

It is the dog's PetMassage in more ways than one. The Expansion Response is used between each of the vertebra, the major large joint complexes, the smaller joints such as the phalanges and even the suture lines between bones in his skull.

If you were to use only the expansion response over your entire dog's body, this would be enough to help him/her reestablish a sense of harmony and reconnection within each of his/her joints. This can be an entire session. And it would be an excellent session, too.

**Follow-on**
Combining stretching and expansion response creates *follow-on*. Follow-on enhances the movement by slightly exaggerating the movement of dynamic energy *released* by the body during compression or expansion.

**Follow-on 1**
**Stretch to Compression to Stretch**
Gently cradle above and below the joint with your two hands. The hand closer to the body, the proximal, will be the supporting hand. The hand further from midline on the body, the distal, will be the acting hand. When starting with the stretch, gently pull the joint elements, and hold, maintaining a slight traction. Wait and hold until you sense the recoil from within the body. Then allow the space to recompress. Continue the movement by gently exaggerating what you feel, further compressing the bones toward each other with only the slightest pressure. Hold the joint in this position.

Wait until you sense the elements within beginning to move back out. Support whatever expanding and unwinding movements that you feel from within the joint. Continue the movement back to homeostasis. You may repeat this movement, moving in and out several times, until you feel that the joint elements have completed "righting" themselves. This movement is called *unwinding*.

**Follow-on 2**
**Compression to Stretch to Compression**
Gently cradle above and below the joint with your two hands. Start with the Expansion response. Gently compress, wait and hold, supporting the movements felt within the joint until you are called to release your pressure. Still gently cradling above and below the joint, support the movement back to neutral. Continue the fluid movement by slowly exaggerating the movement into a very mild stretch. Hold, wait, and witnessing the internal movement happening, support the recoil.

The amount of pressure in this sequence would be the same as that used when gently cradling an injured bird. Each touch is light, gentle, and loving. Each release is a gift.

Think of the follow-on as having a conversation with the body. Open the wordless conversation with the body with gentle coaxing. Respond to what it tells you by supporting its movement either into or away from the articulation. Witnessing and supporting movement honors your dog's innate wisdom and promotes the redistribution of Ch'i within each articulation (joint) in the dog's body.

The effect of even just one internal adjustment is magnificent. One readjustment affects the balance of the entire limb. The effects extend to the entire body, spirit and the dog's surrounds. Each point on your dog's body is a hologram of his body, of his entire life. Affecting one point enhances the quality of his whole life!

**Exercise 13**
**Sensing the response**

Sense the response to gentle compression: decompression

Sense the response to gentle traction: compression

Chapter 14
Beginning the Energy Session
Center yourself. Request and receive permission.
Begin your assessment routine.

1. Breathe and center yourself
2. Ask permission and wait for your dog's response
3. Begin Assessment

**Breathe and center yourself**
Center yourself, creating a quiet, still, controlled place
deep within. This is the anchor for your successful
massage
session.

Each of us is a
bundle of
energy, vibrating
with fluctuating
auras and
varying amounts
of openness and
closedness. We
are always in the
process of
maintaining and
creating the
beings    that we
are.

*Breathe and center yourself*

We create our health-
fulness, our attitudes, and our life conditions. This
goes for dogs as well as people.

When you come close to a dog, your energetic body
that surrounds you overlaps, connecting with the dog's
energetic body. Your two bodies affect each other in
very subtle yet profound ways. On the physical level,
your normal body heat radiating off your body actually
affects the dog's physiology, affecting a slight increase
in his

body heat. This has the effect of subtly increasing his metabolic activity and even the permeability of cell membranes. This means that just your physical presence can affect the movements of nutrients into and waste products out of his cells. Your presence enhances oxygenation, which affects fundamental changes on a cellular level in the dog's life.

Without physically touching the dog you affect his physiology! Of course, dogs have a similar effect on us. And you've wondered why we feel so much more alive around dogs? Well, now you know.

Dogs get over stimulated, too. They sometimes need to touch "safety." Often, they need to connect with the oasis of stillness that you create within. Acknowledging the dog by getting permission enhances the connection you formed the moment you became consciously and unconsciously aware of each other.

**Permission**
When you asked for his permission and his reply was "yes," he created a contract with you. He agreed-- promised--that he will work on the inside, while you work on the outside. Dogs maintain respectful control over their intuitive natures. They may let us know that they are experiencing some discomfort or apprehension, but the ones that we have worked with have always controlled their natural instincts to snap.

> *It's the dog's massage*
> infers that dogs have the choice to receive and to integrate the therapy.
> If they choose not to participate, that decision must also be honored.

There will be times when the answer to your request is "no." This must be honored. Wait a couple of minutes, giving the dog some time to get comfortable with the situation. Often, regrounding yourself with a few cycles of mindful breathing will be enough to create a comfort zone for the dog. If your dog still refuses the session, you may work off the body, moving slowly inward as

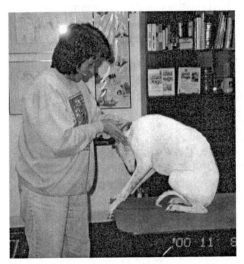

the dog lets down his energetic armoring. If your dog still refuses the session, try again another day. There is no benefit for either of you, if you get frustrated or angry or feel you have to use force.

*"No" must be honored and accepted*

## Assessment

Who is assessing whom and what is being assessed? Assessment is for both you and your dog.

Your observation of the quality of his movements, his flexibility and his attitude will give you an indication of what the two of you will work on during the session. You are creating *intention*. Also assess his openness and his willingness to participate fully in the massage.

> Assessment gives the dog the opportunity to focus his attention as he assesses himself.
>
> ~
>
> His self-assessment increases his body awareness, inside and out.

Even before he gets on your table for his massage session start your assessment.

Note his:

o    Quality of gait
o    Attitude and size of his personal space
o    Balance/symmetry of muscularity of body
o    Exaggerated movements of head, shoulder or hips
o    Look for things that are right as well as what might be wrong.

If you sense that something is not quite right, focus on the positive, bringing it back into balance with the rest of the body. Your dog, who is following wherever your hand touches, appraises his own body. He thinks, "This touch feels good, that pressure hurts, this is tender, ooh, that tickles."

**Assessment strokes...**
are passes of your hands that, with several strokes, cover the dog's entire body. On the physical body, they are done three times, at different pressures: light, medium and firm. This gives you the opportunity to palpate and gauge how the dog feels to you on the surface, just below the skin and in his deeper muscles and structures. On the energetic body, use a minimum of 3 passes at the outer boundary of each perceived energy level.

More importantly, it gives the dog an opportunity to assess his/her own body on these same levels. Remember, it is the dog's massage, not yours. Dogs are acutely aware of the very light strokes. When you've gained permission, your dog has made a contract with you: he will work on the inside wherever your hands are on the outside. Deal.

Support the dog under the jaw or over the withers with one hand and make your passes with the other. Move your active hand in strokes moving from head to tail, and from the top down: relaxation strokes. Maintain contact during the massage session with at least one hand at all times. This gives your dog a sense of safety and security and helps him maintain his connection with your rhythm and flow.

Even, while changing positions keep one hand on the dog. There is the tendency to pull your hands off as you walk around the dog to work on his other side. Maintain continuity with your energetic and physical bond. Keep at least one, and no more than two hands on your dog! Assess the entire dog, moving your hands slowly over his body.

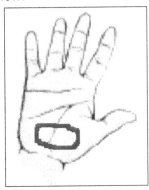

*Highly sensitive to energy*

Palpate, touch with the intention to assess, with the base of your palm rather than with your fingertips. The deep valley in your palm just above the wrist is highly sensitive to heat and energy (Ch'i) nuances. Move over the dog's body in several wide passes. Remember the depths of passes. During assessment strokes, think to yourself:

**The first pass is** Light "Hi. How are ya'?"

**The second is** Medium "Here I am to work with you."

**The third is** Deep or Firm (stripping) "Here you are."

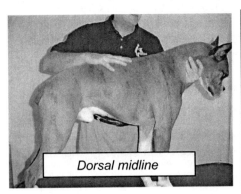

*Dorsal midline*

He focuses his attention on his body as he follows your hands, assessing how his body feels and responds to your touch.

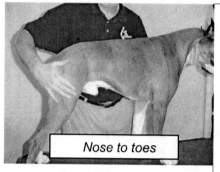

Nose to toes

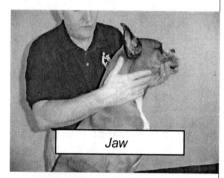

Jaw

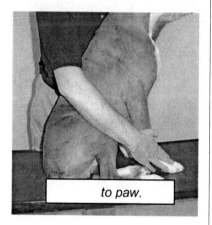

to paw.

*1st set of 3 passes over top line: over top of head to tail (including phantom tail)*

*$2^{nd}$ set of 3 passes, on side, top third of cranium, over shoulder, ribs, hips, hind legs to paws, repeat on other side*

*$3^{rd}$ set of 3 passes, jaw, neck, over shoulder, front legs to paws. repeat on other side*

*$4^{th}$ set of 3 passes: Chin to umbilicus, ventral midline*

Focus your attention on perceiving the dog's body through the base of the palm of your hand. This is the most sensitive to variations of heat and coolness.

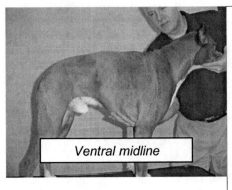

*Ventral midline*

During your assessment strokes, feel for: Shapes of muscles, bones and joints Muscle quality: tight/soft Bumps and divots on skeleton Texture of ligaments, spaces around them Pads of paws Nails Webbing between toes Textures of coat Temperature variations: warm/cool Moisture/dryness Oiliness/dryness Full/emptiness Thick/thinness

At the end of the session, you can note any changes.

Assessment strokes are done at a slow but even pace. Take care to contact the entire body with your strokes. It is easy for us, as our hands glide down the legs, to slide off at the hocks or elbows before we get all the way down to the tips of the paws. Each stroke needs to be deliberate and complete. Consider each stroke a separate massage session. Each stroke is that important. The paws, especially, need to be touched, as they are the end points of many of the meridians. We'll soon learn that some of the most powerful acupressure points are all the way down on the paws by the nails.

### Grounding strokes
End the massage with *grounding strokes*. They are done in the same directions but in the reverse order of the beginning of the massage.

You are both assessing.

Assessment gives you a sense of what you and the dog have to work on, a baseline. It gives the dog an opportunity to observe, feel and integrate the changes in his body. On an unconscious level, you are both appraising your levels of safety and comfort in each other's company. Your comfort levels are determined by the quality of the energetic connection you two have created combining and sharing your energy fields.

Deep "There you are."

1. Medium "Good bye, here I go."
2. Light final grounding strokes (we'll add another element here as we progress)
3. Thank the dog for the opportunity to share this time and experience. (Reverse permission)
4. Breathe and center, grounding yourself

## Exercise 14a
## Assessing the body

Practice the assessment routine with your dog several times. Develop a rhythm and flow to your strokes. Maintain contact with the dog with one of your hands at all times. Remember to keep breathing.

## 14b
## Feeling the aura

Rub the palms of your hands together, creating warmth from the friction. Press your palms together, feeling the heat build between them. Slowly pull them apart to about 1 inch. Hold them in this position and feel the heat between them. Slowly press them toward each other and see if you feel a resistance in the air between them. Slowly pull them apart, to about 4 or 5 inches. Hold for a few seconds and slowly press them toward each other. The air resistance you feel is the same sensation as the edge or boundary of an energy level.

Chapter 15
Touch

To touch is to connect. It is the functional element of massage. Touch is used to assess, locate, excite, relax, and balance the body. It is used on the physical body as a means of accessing the energetic body. It is used on the energetic body as a means of accessing the physical body and the unconscious imagery.

Touch is used on both the physical and energetic body to access emotional and behavioral issues. Let's talk a little bit about the energetic body. The energetic body is made up of, well, energy. Energy knows neither time nor space. It cannot be created or destroyed. It can change form as in Albert Einstein's famous equation, $E=MC^2$. The energy that we are describing is the quality of life essence, of healthfulness that radiates within and around the body. When the body is healthy and the mind is happy and purposeful, the body radiates vibrant happy, powerful energy. When part of the psyche or physiology is depressed the energy radiates with less power.

*Students learning PetMassage$_{TM}$ during workshop*

The energetic body is fluid and overlapping. It can be small, confined to a tiny cavity within the body or, it can be immense, extending for tens of thousands of miles! It is dependent on our physiology and our emotional state.

We can access, palpate, effleurage and petrissage. We can touch the dog's conscious mind to stimulate him to enhance his body awareness. We've seen that our presence alone influences the dog physiologically, emotionally and energetically. As we become more aware of our power to connect through touch, we can see that much of PetMassage_TM is done to *access the internal movements and arrangements of this energy on the unconscious, or subconscious levels.* Touch works on all levels.

The dynamic work of PetMassage_TM happens in the electrical, magnetic and energetic levels. In Western medical vernacular, this is called the parasympathetic system, in Eastern, Ch'i, qi or prana.

**Touch is the energy connection**
Energy healing not only affects the aura and the subconscious, it works at the physical levels, from the subcutaneous to the depths of the interrelationships of organ systems. These are often areas inaccessible to more traditional forms of medical therapy. Touch with and through our arms and hands, creates a circuit that can assist the dog to establish or 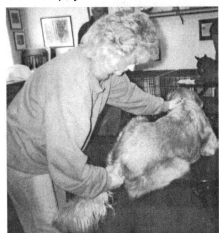 reestablish balance throughout his /her body.

A complete circuit, in which both hands are in contact with the dog's body, helps your dog's energy flow. It moves from your dog's body, through your hand, up your arm, across your shoulders, down the other arm, hand and back to the dog. The quality of the flow is supported by the quality of your groundedness, your connection to Source/ Gaia. Your body is a vessel of healthy energy flowing to boost your dog's flow of Ch'i.

> PetMassage$_{TM}$ balances electrical, magnetic and energetic fields.

> It is not necessary to know exactly which level you are on or what work your dog is processing.

We are now working in areas and processes your dog can neither control nor comprehend. We are now accessing the unconscious or subconscious: where processes are uncontrolled by the conscious mind.

Our responsibility becomes clearer and easier as we think about this: It is not necessary to know exactly which level you are on or what your dog is processing.

> Simply be present.

Your function is to facilitate your dog at

> You are in effect, *witnessing* for your dog.

whatever level his needs take him. And, remember, he too is consciously unaware of his needs or what he is doing. His intuitive body-mind-spirit is making the adjustments he needs.

Open yourself to your dog's subliminal needs. You no longer need to be specific in your awareness. Simply be present. In your touch, you are now *witnessing* for the dog. You cannot witness if your are busy attempting to control the session.

Your *intention* to witness is now very important for your dog's successful massage.

You will see in your practice amazing results from energy work. Naturally, you will have the pride in your work and your accomplishments. And you may get the feeling that you caused your clients to heal, the lame to walk, the sickly to spontaneously recover. At these times, that we do not do the healing. All healing comes from the dogs. We merely facilitate the movement from imbalance to balance. We indicated earlier, in our scope of practice, that we couldn't heal dogs. We can only facilitate their healing and rebalancing. Staying aware of this helps us move away from our egos.

PLEASE NOTE: We are still massaging the dogs with our hands. We still need to assess, palpate, excite, relax, balance and/or stimulate all the external and internal aspects of the dog. The difference is that we have now altered our awareness, our consciousness. This is the way we assist the dogs in gaining access to their mystical circuitry.

During assessment and all palpation, *focus on wellness*. Focus your attention on what's right, as well as what's wrong. If you discover anything out of balance, assist the dog to reestablish his balance/wellness.

There are some forms of medical massage that focus on searching out and destroying muscle knots and problem areas. This may be effective on people, but for dogs, this is too much attention on the negative. Focusing on only the dysfunctional area leaves the rest of the body unaddressed. The rest of the dog has been strained and overworked in its role, compensating for the compromised limb or behavior.

It needs to be balanced too. Dogs' bodies, minds and spirits are so integrated that it is necessary, in each session, to give a full body massage, or at least acknowledge the entire body.

There are some forms of massage that believe the more pressure and pain, the better. "No pain, no gain." In some forms of Shiatsu, or acupressure therapy, patients are often bruised and sore after treatments. Other forms of Shiatsu, use variations of touch that are so controlled, the practitioners can sense as many as seven levels of resistance and/or acceptance on any acupressure point on the body. One level even assesses the soul. Each acupoint is a hologram of the entire body system: physical, spiritual, past, present and future. Energy knows neither space nor time. It spans lifetimes.

If you have ever experienced acupuncture, you know that the needles are inserted less than a tenth of an inch, barely deep enough to pierce the capillaries. The needles do not cause discomfort and weigh less than a fly. They are left in place for a time (from a few minutes to several hours) until the internal energetic connections have been made. Then they are removed. Extremely light touch is actually more effective in bringing the unconscious mind to an area than deep touch. Often the deeper touch distracts the mind prohibiting the inner wisdom within the cells to guide our hands.

Acupressure is applied with your lightest touch; hold until you sense a subtle unwinding movement beneath

---

Asked by a student how much pressure he should use with his dog, Anastasia answered simply, "Push with your heart, not with your hands."

---

your fingers. This is *witnessing* for the dog. You are witnessing his unwinding.

Light touch is becoming more accepted. It is an important aspect of Cranial-sacral work and Orthobionomy®. It is all that dogs require to connect with their deeper instinctual presence. Any more may overwhelm the energy fields. That is all the stimulation that is necessary.

**Exercise 15**
**Qualities of textures**

Think about the qualities of the tissues that you are assessing. How do they feel? How do you feel when you sense them?

Follow the contours of the foreleg from the thick muscles around the shoulder, down the upper arm to the elbow. Observe the shapes, temperatures, and integrity of the elbow joint. Continue down the long bones to the carpus.

Note the quality of the muscles and fascia in the lower leg, in, and around the joint. Continue to the ends of the paws, noting the webbing between the toes, the nails and the pads.

What are the textures of the nails, the pads (sides and bottoms), and the webbing between the toes?

Be open to your dog's responses to your touch and varying amounts of pressure during each of your strokes.

Chapter 16
Energy

**Field Theory**
In Barbara Brennan's, *Hands of Light*, her use of the term "energy" per the Einsteinian model describes matter and energy as interchangeable. She writes, "Mass is nothing but a form of energy. Matter is simply slowed down or crystallized energy. Our bodies are energy." "All particles can be transmuted into other particles. They can be created from energy and transmuted into other particles. They can be created from energy and can vanish into energy." The Field Theory of Energy describes the body as an energy field that has many well-measured components. These include the electrostatic, magnetic, electro-magnetic, sonic, thermal and the visual components of the aura. The aura's measurements indicate definite frequencies and colors. (Chapter 4.)

**Tao** is a concept of Eastern philosophies, which translates as "the way." It is the law of the universe and is translated as "that which is all there is."

"Throughout the philosophies of eastern cultures is the premise that there is force, or vibration, that is common to all matter. It is believed that the smooth flow of this force predetermines good health. When the flow is out of balance, the person experiences physical illness and a sense of uneasiness." (Milady's, *Theory and Practice of Therapeutic Massage*, pp. 562-3).

**Yin and Yang**
The Tao is split into two parts, which are in opposition both dynamically and in motion to each other. This creates the energy that sustains the whole. The two opposing parts are *yin* and *yang*. Yin and yang only exist in relation to one another. With yin

and yang in continuous polarities, we see natural continuous change where nothing is of itself, but is seen as aspects of the whole or as two opposite, complement-ary, aspects of existence.

We've seen the Yin --Yang image for years and years. It was one of the symbols of the 1960's American/UK and European social revolution. It's the symbol used for many martial arts forms and it is on several national flags. It is usually seen as a flat disc with equal swirls of half black and half white with a dot of the opposite in the center of each half's belly. One interpretation was that there is a little bit of the opposite of "whatever" at the core of everything: hate, in love, love, in hate, good in bad, light in dark, big in small, beauty in its opposite, etc. Its significance is more pervasive than this.

One day as I was meditating on the image, I saw it as a three-dimensional sphere; swirling about, constantly in motion, in perpetual process of creating and striving for balance. The one point absolutely in balance was the spot directly in its center. This point is called the "still point." It is the point of equilibrium in the midst of chaotic motion of the extremes. This is the place where healing and healthfulness occurs. This was my personal "aha."

One can only exist in relation to the other. Cold has no meaning without being in relation to that aspect that is less cold, or hot. If one aspect is weak, then the opposite aspect will be strong. Breathing, digestion, underactivity, and even seasons are examples of this interaction. This relationship between the yin and yang is considered to be the source of all change, all movement. The tension between them creates "all that there is."

> The *relationship* between the yin and yang is the source of all change and movement.

### Aspects of Yin and Yang

| Yin | vs. | Yang |
|---|---|---|
| Dark or night | | Light or day |
| Low | | High |
| Cold | | Hot |
| Inside | | Outside |
| Contracting | | Expanding |
| Passive | | Active |
| Deficient | | Excessive |
| Female | | Male |
| Emotional soft | | Rational hard |

Here are positions and locations of these concepts that can we use in our practice.

### Aspects of

| Yin | and | Yang |
|---|---|---|
| Front of body | | Back of body |
| Inner body | | Outer body |
| Solid | | Hollow |
| Lower body | | Upper body |
| Underactive | | Overactive |
| Coldness | | Hotness |
| Weak | | Forceful |

When either yin or yang is stronger the body is out of balance.

If your dog has too much moisture, for example, he will perspire, have edema (retention of interstitial fluids causing swelling), and mucousy phlegm on his tongue or in his stools.

*Wherever the sun hits is yang, the shadowed area is yin.*

If there's too little moisture, or dryness, he will have flaky skin, brittle nails, excessive thirst, dry scratchy throat and constipation (due to not enough fluid in his bowels). Both are imbalances.

When there is imbalance one aspect overwhelms and suppresses the other. When this is the case, the area is said to have either too little or too much flow. Too much flow is *excess*. Too little flow is called deficiency, or *stagnation*. Stagnation of the flow of what, you ask? *Energy*, or life force makes up the stuff that is the "all that is."

When the body is in harmony, your dog's skin is in balance. It is clear and glowing. There is no flaking, itching, blotches or edema. Hence, mo' betta wellness.

The more balance, the greater the flow of energy.

When I purchased my first horse, Tiffin, a liver Chestnut Morgan gelding, I was concerned about his hooves. Many of the other horses in the barn were getting thrush, a hoof disease. This is an infection in which the hooves become soft, unhealthy and foul smelling. There were also some problems with horses that had dry, flaky hooves. I needed to know how to care for my horse so he wouldn't have any of these problems.

Since I was a registered, certified and city-raised, greenhorn, I asked for advice from everybody I met who had any horse experience. One day, I led my horse up to a weathered old stable hand leaning up against a fence and asked, "What do you do if your horses hooves get too dry? He squinted at me spat on the ground, and drawled, "Stand him in a puddle."

"Okay," I said, "what do you do if his hooves get too moist?" He looked up and grinned. "Take him out of the puddle."

How's that for a practical lesson in yin and yang theory?

--JR

### Exercise 16
### Energy ball

Rub your hands together, creating warmth from the friction. Press your palms together then pull them 1" apart. Feel the continuing release of heat from the center of your palms and their connection to each other.

Cup your hands, forming a ball of energy about the size of a tennis ball. Moving your hands in and out expands and contracts the size of the ball. Open your arms to the size of a beach ball. Encircle the energy ball with your arms.

Toss the ball up in the air and catch it. Sense the movement and heat of the ball as it floats up into the air and softly returns to be cradled within your arms and palms.

Project the energy ball onto your knee by cupping your hand around your knee and feeling the heat and healing power radiating through the joint.

Cup your hands over your dog's sore elbow, hip or any bruised or arthritic joint. Sense the flow of energy from one palm to the other through the dog's joint. Pure energy connects with your dog's intentions toward self-healing.

# Unit 5
# Ch'i, Acupoints and Meridians

Chapter 17
Energetic Body

**On the cellular level**
What's going on within the body? Let's discuss
activities on the cellular level and move on to more
gross (macro) observations.

We've all learned about *the Krebs cycle* at one time or
another. It describes the chemistry of muscle work. To
briefly review, the oxidization of pyruvic acid liberates
energy. ATP, adenosine triphosphate, present in all
cells, but particularly in muscle cells, produces
phosphates and *energy* when acted upon and split by
an enzyme (adenosine triphosphatase). In this cycle,
carbohydrates, proteins and fats are utilized in the
production of ATP. During muscle contraction, ADP,
adenosine diphosphate is produced. It is reformed
during the muscle relaxation phase.

Relax, this is about as technical as this course is going
to get. The Krebs cycle is fascinating in its elegance of
chemistry. For those of you who would like to learn
more about this system, there are plenty of books and
articles about it. Our approach may appear to have
little in common with chemistry. Consider that the
essence of life energy, Ch'i, moves along with the
breath. It can be likened to the oxidizing effect;
creating, rejuvenating and maintaining energy flow
within all the cells and muscles of the body. This
oxidizing/renewing/healing effect, works beyond the
physical body. PetMassage$_{TM}$ Energy Work affects the
off-the-body levels too.

Bio-magnetism, the study of magnetic fields produced
by living things, has another explanation for the
movement of energy. The body and our universe is a
complex paradigm of electronic attraction and
repulsion. Each cell in our pets' (and our) bodies has
polarity and charge. The quality and quantity of charge
and polarity determines

how it functions in relation to other cells, organs and the whole of the life organism.

Connecting your energies in PetMassage combines them, Connecting supports both the physicality and spirituality of your two lives.

The cumulative effect of the combining of your two living energies (those of you and your dog) is seen by changes in the circulation of flow throughout your bodies. As your bodies touch you are interfacing with, and affecting, all of each other's circuitry, internal and external. Entering the room, or even thinking about each other, has an affect.

As the energies in your two bodies become excited, the tiny spaces between the cells decrease which increases intracellular pressure. This increased cellular activity, the motion and friction of the movement of the molecules in a higher pressure, creates heat.

The heat increases circulation and increases cellular activity, enhancing the permeability of cellular membranes. This results in more efficient digestion, increased lymphatic movement and higher levels of neurologic functioning. As your dog's hormone production and distribution is increased, the effects are increased *emotional* stability.

The body is made of energy. At its densest; it is made of bones, organs, fluids and tissues that we perceive with our basic human senses. These are made of cells and their components, smaller units that we can see with the aid of a basic microscope. These elements are made of still smaller units that can be discerned with an electron microscope and even tinier units that can be described by Quantum physics theory. The energy that we are discussing is the stuff that holds these tiniest of units together.

It is invisible, yet remarkably accessible. Every part of your dog's energy field has intelligence. It contains all the wisdom and knowledge of the universe.

**Exercise 17**
**Affecting body temperature with thought**

Recall a conversation with a good friend or lover. Remember how good it feels to be in that person or pet's company. Feel the warmth of the memory in your heart and tummy.

Observe how your body is bathed in warmth and love.

Your thoughts have increased your core body temperature.

Observe your dog as you think kind and loving thoughts about him or her. Notice if you feel a change in his body temperature. It can be extreme as you have just felt with your own body, or it might be barely noticeable. As your thoughts occur, there will be responses to them that you can feel.

Chapter 18
Ch'i, an introduction

Ch'i is difficult to measure, but it is very real. It's nature and usefulness as a means of diagnosing and treating the body's ailments has been well documented by an overwhelming body of anecdotal, experiential and historical evidence. Since it is difficult to measure, Ch'i is sometimes dismissed as either being unreal or inaccessible. We know that the entire body and all its systems are influenced and regulated through the strength and flow of Ch'i.

There are several basic types of Ch'i; among them are:

> Source Ch'i,
> Food Ch'i,
> Protective Ch'i,
> Breath Ch'i,
> Shen, and
> Meridian Ch'i.

These are all aspects of the same stuff. They all work together to create the qualities of health and maintenance of the body. The goal is balance and harmony.

**Source Ch'i** is the hereditary information received at birth. It is strongest at birth and lessens over the lifespan until it is used up at death. It can be depleted with illness, environmental influences, diet and emotional stress. It is life. It is aliveness.

Kahlil Gibran, the Persian philosopher, said, "When you are born, your work is placed in your heart."

**Food Ch'i** is extracted and utilized from nutrients in food and drink. We are what we eat. The energy in food is dependent on its ingredients, how the food is prepared and how it is served. The mood of the person preparing it affects the food's energy. That's why home cooked meals always taste better that fast food. That's one of the reasons some dogs thrive on poor quality kibble and others are unable to digest the best foods money can buy. Your love and caring attitude are mixed in your dog's food bowl and are as essential as the chemical nutrients.

**Protective Ch'i** is your dog's immune system.

**Breath Ch'i** relates to breathing. We breathe in clean Ch'i and breath out our used/stale Ch'i. Clean air facilitates breathing.

**Shen** is the spirit aspect of Ch'i.

**Meridian Ch'i** follows the pathways of acupressure points that are located just beneath the surface of the body. Although all the types of Ch'i work together, for this course, we will be primarily referring to the Ch'i of the Breath and the movements of Ch'i through meridians. In our PetMassage$_{TM}$ energy sessions there is little we can do to affect the Source Ch'i or the Food Ch'i. We can affect the Protective Ch'i, Breath Ch'i and Shen through our touch.

**Newly discovered historical reference for acupressure**
In 1991 a Neolithic man was discovered in an Italian glacier. Known as the "Ice Man," he was discovered intact, in perfect condition. He was discovered clothed so we now know what type of clothing was used. He had a satchel with flint, sharpening stone, a kind of knife, seeds for foodstuff, etc. and so we now know more about what nomadic people of that time carried when they traveled. The undigested food, the contents of his stomach and intestines let us know what he ate. He has been the subject of some fascinating scientific research.

One of the most interesting things found on this 5000 year old "Ice Man' was some interesting markings tattooed on his ankle and leg. These markings correspond to what we now accept as acupressure points along the meridian [series of acupressure points] that would stimulate the prostate gland. On examination, he was indeed, found to have an enlarged prostate. He had been instructed by someone with the knowledge of acupressure, how and where to self-administer acupressure or acupuncture treatment on these points. This demonstrates that acupressure was not only practiced, it was already an established and accepted form of health care more than 5000 years ago!

**Exercise 18**
**Always in the valleys**

As you work your hands over your dog, feel for the subtle and obvious grooves and bumps over the bony prominences, muscles, tendons and ligaments. Feel the fatty areas, through which energy has a harder time moving. Feel the spaces between the ridges along the spine. Feel the hollow area in the hock just above the malleolus. Feel the spaces between the pads under the feet.

Feel the curls and swirls in the ear. Acupressure points are always in the valleys.

Chapter 19
Acupressure points/Acupoints

Acupressure points are energy transmission sites that can be accessed to enhance, slow or maintain the movement of energy through the body. They are referral points. They assess the energy that comes into them and refer the energy on.

Acupoints are located in the depressions in the joints between bones, between ligaments, tendons and between muscle groups. In other words, acupoints are found in valleys. Each point has its own *vitality*, or sense of texture. They can have the texture of feeling hard or spongy or tight, warm or cool, sensitive/painful or even empty of sensation. These textures yield important information about each point. Understanding them helps the practitioner to assess and support the balancing of the flow of Ch'i through each of the points.

> Acupoints are located in valleys.

When you are assessing your dog, and your hand is palpating the body, you are sensing the shapes and textures and the reactions to your touch. You are also

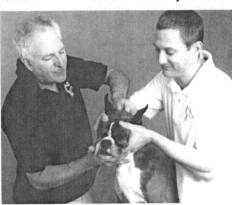

palpating the spaces between these elements. And, you already know what's in the spaces. Once you've differentiated the shapes by the outlines or depressions you can assess the textures or qualities of the tissues.

On the most fundamental, elemental level, animal communication is the palpation of and acknowledging of the reaction to acupoints.

### Qualities of Textures

Oily or dry
Smooth or rough
Hard or spongy
Tight or loose
Warm or cool
Sensitive/painful or comfortable
Empty or full

To begin, these acupoints that you can access have very specific effects. As you touch each of them sense for the above qualities and observe your dog's reaction.

See how you both react to different hand pressures; light, medium, deep and off the body. Notice what happens when you hold your breath.

_ints you will use in your practice_

**High intensity points** on the dog's body:

- GC (Governing Vessel) 26, Divot under dog's nose –powerful, for cardiac arrest
- CV (Conception Vessel) 1, Divot under rectum (ventral aspect) –powerful, also for cardiac
- BL (Bladder) 1,2, around eyes, calming
- BL (Bladder) 1-48 eyes to hip, both sides of spine, water metabolism
- GV (Governing Vessel) 26, divot under nose, cardiac arrest/ life force point
- GB (Gall Bladder) 29, 30 under hip joint, hip dysplasia
- SP (Spleen) 21connecting point on 6$^{th}$ rib. Connects Yang to Yin
- ST (Stomach) 36, "Walk three miles," increases stamina in legs and rest of body
- LU (Lung) 7, inside of front paw, just above wrist bone, respiratory, asthma
- LI (Large Intestine) 11, outside of elbow joint, local elbow and shoulder problems
- SP (Spleen) 6, rear legs, inside of foot, to the front and above heel, hormones i.e. insulin
- LI (Large Intestine) 4, inside front paw, Front leg problems, head, sinuses, and neck, Longevity point
- KI (Kidney) 1, just behind the pads on the back paws, called Bubbling Spring, grounding and life force point.

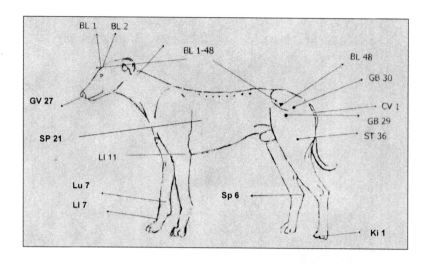

Stimulate these points with the following effects:

- Base of ears, pinna – Triple Heater meridian, for calming, shock, temperature extremes, fever
- Aspirin point, on the other side of the SP-6 point in the lateral hock, used to alleviate pain
- Tip of the ears, known as the "shock point," firm pressure shoots a blast of adrenalin through the dog.
- Triad. Connecting 3 points on top of head.
  Hold a finger a finger width just to the inside of each
  ear and another on the Third Eye, just behind the stop. The front of the occipital protuberance (Crown
  Chakra) is under the center of your palm.
- Stop. Transition point from the muzzle to the skull; controls your dog's head and movement of his body.
- Transitions from cervical to thoracic, thoracic to lumbar, (Solar Plexus Chakra), Lumbar to Sacral, sides of base of tail bilaterally

Shock point    triad,        third eye ,  stop, philtrum

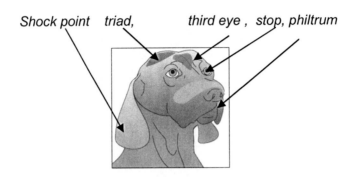

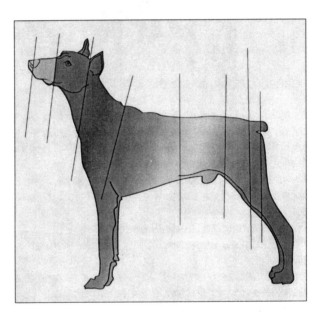

*Transition planes*

When working on these points, hold them lightly for at least 10 seconds and release only when you feel the body has released its tension and, having completed its movement, pushes your hands away. The holding time may extend to as much as several minutes.

**Exercise 19**
**Sensing levels of acupoints**

Palpate all the points listed in the chart using the three different pressures at each point. Sense how the different levels feel to you. Sense how your dog reacts to your different intensities of pressure. Sense how your dog responds to your varying amounts of concentration and intention.

Can your dog sense your presence when you hold your hand 2 inches above his body? 12 inches? 24 inches?

## Chapter 20
## Traditional Asian Medicine

In Traditional Asian Medicine, your dog's lifestyle is included in the philosophy, diagnosis and treatment of life conditions. Lifestyle incorporates the influences of climate, temperature, family history, present family circumstances, emotional stressors and diet. It allows for variations in body functions according to a natural rhythm as each day progresses.

Your dog is in a constant state of disequilibrium; each moment is different from the one before. Even if you used the same techniques and the exact same types and numbers of strokes in the identical order, the massage that you would give at 9 in the morning would be different from the one you would give at 3 in the afternoon. You are no longer the same person as you were earlier today.

Physiologically, you've both had billions of cells die and be replaced, you've consumed food and water and processed and eliminated what's left from yesterday's meals. Emotionally and spiritually, you've had new experiences, new dreams and creative thoughts. You've had fresh conversations, formed opinions, changed your mind, made new friends, and played with your pets. You've had a very busy day.

Your dog has been busy, too. During the same time your dog has eaten, napped, played, napped, chased squirrels, napped and spent quality time with you. He's replaced millions of cells in his body. He's thought about some of the same things he's thought about before, reinforced and deepened his memory patterns. He's moved about in the same ways he's moved about before, reinforcing and deepening muscle memory and behavior patterns He's a different dog. Both you and the dog are substantially different entities: chemically, emotionally, and chronologically. The proverb, "You can't step into the same river twice" now makes sense.

Each PetMassage_TM session is different. Each dog has his own needs that vary from minute to minute. Your potential for connecting with and helping your dog also varies from minute to minute, depending on the time of day, each of your biorhythms, and your moods. The term *Circadian Rhythm* describes the way dogs' bodies' function through-out the progression of a day's cycle. Your dog's biorhythms progress through the stream of meridians each day. The study of Traditional Asian Medicine is extensive and richly complex. This text is only the briefest of introductions to the concept of Ch'i and acupressure points. We hope we have teased you enough that you will expand your knowledge on this subject. If we have, please refer to the list of books in the Suggested Reading section in the back of this text.

In Traditional Asian Medicine, there are many concepts that cumulatively can be used in the diagnosis and treatment of disease or wellness. There are the Yin - Yang natures, the Eight Guiding Principles, The Five Phases of Transformation, The Creation Cycle, and more. (*The Well-Connected Dog*, pp. 9-25). In our PetMassage_TM Scope of Practice, as therapist-instructors, we can neither diagnose nor treat specific conditions. So, in this context we will not cover diagnostic uses or treatments.

> Although we can neither diagnose nor treat specific conditions, there is still much we *can* do.

There is still a lot that we can do. Besides increasing circulation, improving muscle tone, and relaxing the recipient, PetMassage~TM~ energy techniques enable you to connect with your dog in profound ways. You are able to support your dog in his or her own health maintenance. You can facilitate the self-healing of many of his physical, behavioral and emotional issues.

PetMassage~TM~, you see, is less about "relaxing," as about "rebalancing."

> PetMassage~TM~ energy techniques enable you to connect with your dog in profound ways.

**Meridians**
A meridian is described as "a channel of energy coursing beneath the skin's surface. Each meridian pathway follows aspects of the circulatory, lymphatic, muscular and nervous systems." (Four Paws Five Directions, p. 13) Each meridian is made up of a series of acu-points that relate to a specific organ system. So, if we are referring to the Bladder Meridian, for example, we are not just referring to the points affecting the organ called the Urinary Bladder. We are supporting the entire system that supports fluid balance within the body.

We're talking about all the fluids, including blood, lymph, cerebral spinal fluid, urine, tears, and intra and extracellular fluid. Even the drool that slimes and the poop that squishes when you step in it; all the fluid.

A meridian has also been likened to an expressway with on-off ramps. [Schwartz] The lines of energy flow are the expressways and the acupoints are the ramps that we use to access the interior of your dog's body from the exterior. When there is a blockage at any of the acupoints, the flow of energy backs up, just like traffic on a blocked expressway ramp. This is the state of stagnation. If the ramp is slippery with ice, the movement on it is too fast and is out of control. This is excess. Where the energy flows smoothly, the state of flow is in balance.

A meridian is a series of points that run from the surface of the body to the interior. Their patterns create pathways, or channels. Some of the most powerful points of these channels are at the ends. Using the example of a pencil, one end has the lead tip, broken, dull or sharpened, the other end is the eraser, fresh, hard, or worn flat, and in between is the connecting part. Continuing the pencil metaphor, much of the work is done at the ends. The ends are where one meridian transitions to another meridian. The qualities of the transitions depend upon the healthfulness of the end points.

Meridians are divided into two groups, called yin and yang. As energy moves around and through the body, it follows these pathways moving through yin and yang channels, until the entire body is connected. With this in mind, you can see that every point on your dog's body influences the entire body. Each acupoint is a hologram of the whole.

Most of the meridians are bi-lateral; they are duplicated on each side of the body. The movement of energy from point to point and from meridian to meridian follows the route shown in the following diagram.

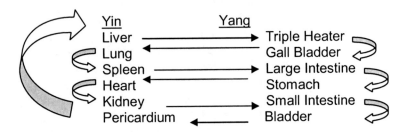

## Circadian rhythm

Ch'i energy flows from one meridian to the next in rhythm with the circadian clock. Each meridian has a specific time period in which it is most active. This is your dog's natural rhythm as it relates to a 24-hour day. Moving in groups of two yang to two yin, two yang to two yin, and so on.

Starting at Midnight, Yang-Triple Heater, to Yin – Gall Bladder and so on.

| Time | Yin | Yang | Time |
|------|-----|------|------|
| 1-3 AM | Liver | Triple Heater | 9-11 PM |
| 3-5 AM | Lung | Gall Bladder | 11-1AM |
| 9-11AM | Spleen | Large Intestine | 5-7 AM |
| 11-1 PM | Heart | Stomach | 7-9 AM |
| 5-7 PM | Kidney | Small Intestine | 1-3 AM |
| 7-9 PM | Pericardium | Bladder | 3-5 PM |

The meridians are multifaceted in their references. They connect to the organ and the systems that maintain and support the functioning of that organ. They also mark referral points in the body. These points would react, as being either painful or tender to your touch when the meridian organ system you are accessing is out of balance.

Meridians also represent dog emotions and spiritual orientations.

Follow the directions of the meridians; both the Yin and Yang primary meridians flow from rear to front, inferior to superior.

## Meridians

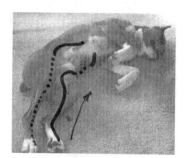

*Liver, Yin*

*to*
*Triple*
*heater, Yang*

*Gall bladder, yang to*
*Lung, Yin* ⟵

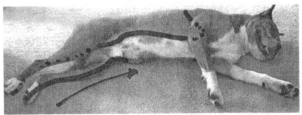

*Spleen/pancreas, Yin*

*to Large Intestine*

→

*Stomach, yang*

*to*

*Heart, yin*

→

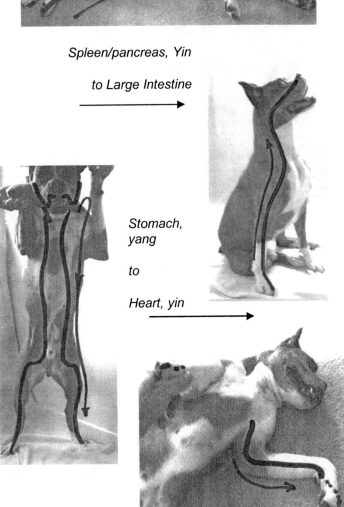

144

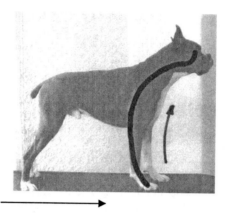

*Kidney, yin*
   *to Small Intestine, yang*

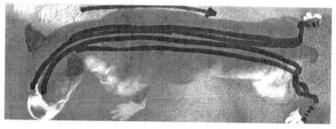

*Bladder, yang*

*to Pericardium, yin*

There are two meridians that do not channel to specific organ systems and do not run bilaterally. They are the Conception and Governing Vessels. Their course takes them in single paths across the midlines of the topline (dorsal) and the undercarriage (ventral).

The Conception vessel is the ultimate Yin Meridian. It runs midline under the ventral aspect of the dog from anus to chin. The Governing Vessel, the ultimate Yang, runs over the dorsal aspect of the dog from the tip of his tail midline along the spine, over his head to his upper lip. The Governing Vessel runs in the same direction as the Concep-tion, even though it is Yang. The Governing Vessel corresponds to the Western Central Nervous System. The Conception Vessel corresponds to the Peripheral Nervous System.

They balance and connect all the Yin or Yang meridians.

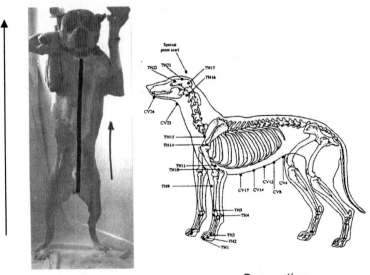

*Vessel*

*Conception*

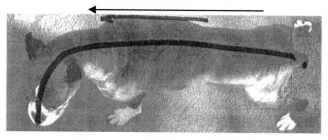

*Governing Vessel*

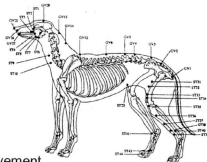

**The Clasp Hands** movement, in which your hands move from the spine, down the ribs on both sides, to the ventral midline, clasp, and back up to the dorsal midline, connects the back to the belly and the belly to the back. In other words, it

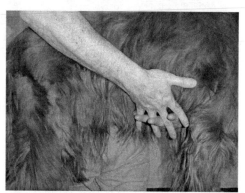

connects the Governing Vessel (yang) to the Conception Vessel (yin). There is a point midway on the sixth rib, where you can palpate your dog's heartbeat, that is called the *Connecting Point of Connecting Points*. Stimulating it also connects yang to yin. Connecting the yin to yang, connects the dualities of your dog's body, mind and spirit.

## Dualities of your dog's body, mind and spirit

**Yang**
Dorsal
Governing Vessel,
Central Nervous System

**Yin**
Ventral
Conception Vessel,
Peripheral Nervous System

### Connecting the Dots

Throughout his massage, your dog's attention has been following your hands all over his body. He's experienced your touch on his head, his shoulders, his paws, his hips, his hocks and his tail. At the end of the massage you will want to focus his attention on his midline, his primary yin and yang meridians, before your closure with grounding strokes. As you complete your final assessment stroke, you will find your hand resting on your dog's umbilicus, his *hara*, or energetic center. This is a good place to start connecting his "dots."

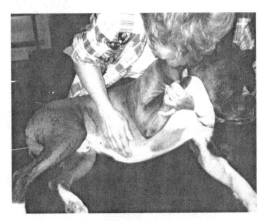

*Connecting his "dots"*

"Dots" refer to the Conception and Governing Vessels.

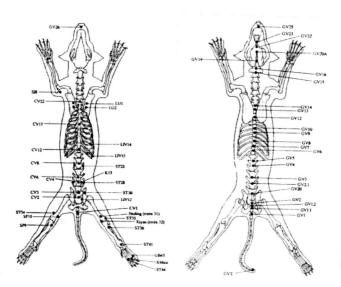

*Ventral Conception Vessel*      *Dorsal Governing Vessel*

On the Conception Vessel, touch lightly and briefly starting at the Hara just below the umbilicus. Move quickly up toward the head touching the base of the sternum, midway up the sternum; the top of the sternum, the base of the neck, under the jaw, and under the chin.

On the Governing Vessel, start at he base of the tail. Touch random spots up the spine and continue over the sagittal crest of the head, the stop, the pigmented portion of the nose and end at the philtrum, that little divot between the nostrils above the upper lip. Connecting these dots directs your dog's attention back to midline to recenter it and ready it for grounding.

| Yang Meridian Triple Heater | Function Commander of all energies. | Emotion/Behavior Transforms and transmits Ch'i to organs, helps to excrete waste and balance body heat. Anger, inability to move smoothly forward |
|---|---|---|
| Gall Bladder | Rules eyes, ligaments, muscles, tendons and joints | Official of decision and judgment |
| Large Intestine | Absorption | Apprehension or Stubbornness |
| Stomach | Digestion | Fear, Anxiety, Nervous tension |
| Small Intestine | Nourishes the body | Rules discernment, works with heart for clarity |
| Bladder | Controls fluids of the body, balances the entire meridian system | Addresses fear, depression and agitation. |
| Governing Vessel | Strengthens back and spine, Regulates Central Nervous system. Helps redistribute and balance Yang Ch'i energy | Hyperactivity |

| Yin Meridians Liver | Function Metabolism, harmonious movement of Ch'i | Emotion/Behavior Emotion/Behavior Evenness of temperament, harmonizing emotions |
|---|---|---|
| Lung | Rules Ch'i: Quality and Quantity of breath, determines quality and quantity of life | Compulsive Behaviors, Depression |
| Spleen | Immune system | Timid, lack of awareness |
| Heart | Center of emotional and mental consciousness. Wisdom | Regulates memory Hyperactive, Depression, Courage |
| Kidney | Works on the bones and bone marrow | Survival and instinctual fear. Fear aggression |
| Pericardium | Protects Heart, absorbs heat | Brings joy. Rules physical and emotional attacks |
| Conception Vessel | Reproductive functions, balance of peripheral nervous system | Anxiety or hyperactivity |

**Exercise 20**
**Connect the dots**

Trace the pathways of the Conception Vessel and the Governing Vessel.

Sense for your dog's reactions to your touch. Practice your new Clasp Hands variation. Connect your dog's belly to the back and the back to the belly.

Chapter 21
Accessing and Following Meridians

**Directions and significance of meridian energy flow.** On the Yang meridians, the directions of meridian work are predominantly from cervical (front) to caudal (back) and from dorsal (top) to ventral (bottom). For the Yin, the reverse, back to front and distal to proximal. Moving with the flow (numbering on the meridian charts) enhances energy movement. Movements against the "grain" impedes flow. Either direction may be appropriate depending on what the body needs to create balance within its meridian system.

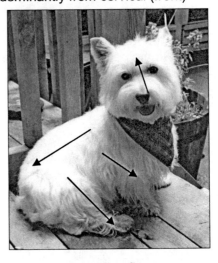

*Yang meridian flow*

You'll notice that the PetMassage™ system is a slight deviation from the more orthodox use of acupressure.

Here are two exercises that will help you get a feel for where the meridians are on your dog. This

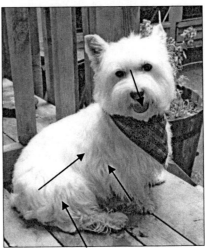

*Yin meridian flow*

will also help you to connect the Yang to the Yin, helping your dog's energy flow to become more evenly balanced. Recall the photograph of Gracie on page 38. Wherever the sun hits is yang, and the shadowed area is yin.

We know that the Yang meridians run primarily from front to back and from top to bottom. Yang is on the dorsal and lateral (upper and outer) parts of the body. We know that the Yin meridians run primarily from back to front and from bottom to top. Yin is on the ventral and medial (lower and inner) parts of the body.

#1. Cranial, or near the head:  Start at the insides of the front paws. Yin. Slide your hands up the inside (medial) legs to the sternum, chest, throat and to the chin.  Yang. Allow your hands to flow up the sides of the jaw to the ears.  Slide your hands around the front of the ears and allow them to slide back over the top of the head down to the sides of the neck to the shoulders. Continue the stroke down the outside (lateral)

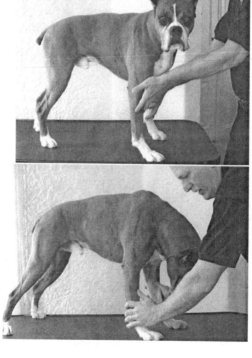

of the forelegs to the outside toes. Repeat this circular pattern several times.

*#1*
*Yin to Yang*
*to Yin to Yang*

#2 Caudal, or near the tail: Start at the insides of the hind paws. Yin. Slide your hands up the medial (inside) legs to under the inside of the fold of the flank, over the abdomen, to the sternum of the ribcage. Yang. Allow your hands

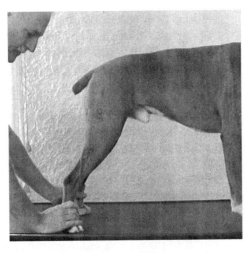

to flow up the sides of the ribs just behind the scapula (shoulder blade), up to the spine. Slide your hands down either side of the spine to the base of the tail. Follow the lines of coat down the back of the thigh (hamstrings) the backs of the stifles, hocks, and pasterns to the backs of the pads. Slide them back over to the top of the paw. Repeat this circular motion 6 times. These movements also take you from Yin to Yang.

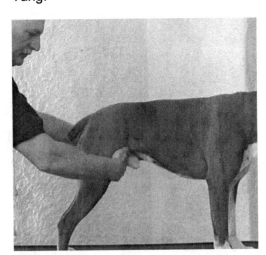

*#2*
*Yang to Yin*
*to* Yang

Awareness and use of meridians (connecting the acudots) is integrated with all PetMassage$_{TM}$ bodywork. Wherever you touch your dog, you will access and stimulate acupoints on meridians. Whenever you sense that your hand is pulled to, held on or pushed away from a particular spot, you are responding to your dog's needs at that point. Acuwork is being done.

The complexity of your PetMassage$_{TM}$ energy session will be enhanced as you work with the knowledge of locations of specific acupressure points and meridians. You are already observing qualities such as hot vs. cool, dry vs. damp, full vs. empty, solid vs. spongy and painful vs. comfortable as you palpate the muscularity of your dog's body. When you combine the significances of these textures to acupoints and meridian lines and what *they* represent, you have a better idea of how and why your dog has reactions to your touch.

> The complexity of your session is enhanced with the knowledge of locations of acupressure points and meridians.

As you move your hand over the top line, for example, your awareness is not only of the coat and the spine, the ridges of the vertebrae, the textures of the ligaments and muscles running over and next to the spine. You are also now aware that you are assessing the Governing Vessel and the Bladder Meridian. You now know that you are also accessing and enhancing the flow of all the fluids throughout his entire body. You are also addressing such physical issues as hyperactivity, and the emotional states of depression or fear.

As you palpate around the nose and muzzle, across the side of the face and around the ears and eyes, you are not only feeling the textures of his coat; you are also assessing his Large Intestine Meridians, Bladder

Meridian, Stomach Meridians, the Triple Heaters and others.

Let's say, when your hand feels the base of one of the ears, you sense a spongy, soft and cool spot. That would indicate that there is a deficiency or stagnation in the Triple Heater Meridian. The Triple Heater is the heat regulator on the body, so it would not be surprising to find other areas on the body that are out of balance, either too cool or too warm. Coolness indicates a deficiency or old wound and heat indicates excess, possibly a recent trauma, or infection.

So, now you are a pro at finding acupressure spots. You can palpate them to determine their textures and temperatures. You can sense if they are stagnant, balanced or in excess. You know what meridians are, where they are located and the directions that their energy flows. You are starting to get a feel for the emotional processes that are being accessed. You even have an idea of the times of the day when meridians are most active.

Three big questions arise.

1. When do you use this information in practice?
2. How can you tell if what you are doing is effective?
3. And, can you harm an animal by doing it wrong?

**When do you use this information in practice?**
With added awareness of *what* you are touching and *why* different points on the dog feel the way they do, you are now more present and supportive of your dog's self-healing. We are not the ones who heal; healing is up to the dog.

Each time you touch your dog, now; you will be more attuned to what his body is telling you. This is true animal communication. His body may say, "I have this need," or, "I have this emotional stuff I have to work through." Again, it is up to the dog to do the choosing and the healing. His body may say, "I don't want to

work today, I just want to enjoy your loving touch."
That can be a valid reason to get a massage, too.

Meridian work is not a separate component of
PetMassage$_{TM.}$ It adds another dimension to the rest
of your dog's massage. It is another tool in your set of
skills.

Here is an example of using acupoint and meridian
work in your practice: Let's say you are assessing your
dog's front leg. You slowly glide your hand over the
point of the shoulder. As you move your hand down
the inner upper arm you sense that your hand is being
pulled, as if by a magnet, and held in place. You feel a
coolness and sluggishness under the skin. You know
that your hand is over the Lung, Heart, Pericardium,
and the Gall Bladder meridians. You review what
stagnation in these meridians may infer. Observe your
hand being lightly held there until you sense that it has
been released. That's it. You have used acupressure
in your dog's massage.

> The system of circuitry is invisible,
> subcutaneous and subconscious

At this point, it is not necessary for you to know
precisely what you are working on or what the
dynamics are. You are accessing a system of circuitry
that is invisible, subcutaneous and subconscious.
Even your dog is not aware of what is happening in his
body. His reaction to your work may be immediate, or
he may need several hours or days to process and
integrate his new internal paradigm.

The pressure that you use will be different each time,
depending on your dog's needs and his subliminal
requests. You may feel your hand pulled into the
muscles; in which case, your pressure will be fairly
deep. You may just sense that your hand is lightly held

in place. You may feel that your hand is being pushed a couple of inches or a couple of feet off his body.

The very lightest of touch is effective with Energy work. When receiving acupuncture, a needle is inserted only 1/10 of an inch and has virtually no weight or pressure. It is held in place by the electrical tension of the energy vortex just beneath the skin. A ½ inch off the mark and the needle will not stay upright. You needn't be concerned with locating a precise point. Your dog will direct your hands to exactly the right spots. Then, witness whatever healing or readjustment occurs in the dog.

It is not necessary to know what, how, why, when or where. Know that you are present for your dog. Your function is to bring his awareness of whatever level of his subconscious he is using to correct his condition. Your dog is aware of your healing presence. At some level his body will understand what needs to be done. At some level the work will be done.

This ought to drive anyone who has a penchant for control, absolutely batty.

> This ought to drive anyone who needs to control, absolutely batty.

**How can you tell if what you are doing is effective?**
The signals that dogs give when they are releasing physical or emotional holding patterns are often easy to detect. They may yawn, pass gas, stretch, jerk, twitch, roll their eyes, and lick their noses. Their respiration may slow to adjust to a very relaxed state. They may even pass out.

One of my clients at a dog show in Detroit, a Borzoi, went into a trance and tipped over. I'll never forget the look on her face as she was falling.

She projected the thought, "What's going on heeeeeeeeer." Thud. I held her as she stayed in a deep sleep for about 4 or 5 minutes. When she roused she appeared disoriented, but allowed me to gently work her head, neck, chest and forelimbs (Small Intestine, Heart, Pericardium, Lung and Triple Heater meridians). She regained her feet and reunited with her owner/handler. She was entered and shown later that day without incident.

I later learned that she had been suffering from anxiety due to a traumatic accident.

You will see what appears to be spontaneous healings. You'll observe spectacular behavioral changes in your dogs. The weak will rise and walk, the old and infirm will jump and play like puppies, allergies and skin rashes will clear up within hours, depressions will lift and the anxieties will appear to vanish. Sometimes you won't see any changes initially.

All of the changes and rates of healing
are out of our control.

All of the changes and rates of healing are out of our control. Witness and move on. Processing the energy work is totally up to the dog. And, it's up to the dog's subconscious, at that.

159

### Can you harm an animal by doing it wrong?

In all PetMassage$_{TM}$ work, the first rule is to *do no harm*. Energetic bodywork is done by the dog. Recall that the dog used his Five Rights when dispensing his internal drugstore. That's the Right Patient, Right Medication, Right Dose, Right Route and Right Time. The requirements of same correct internal dynamics are tapped intuitively.

> There is no point in planning or expecting specific results.

With balanced energy flow, your dog produces and distributes the Right Hormones and Energy through the Right access ramps along his internal freeways. His body knows the correct dosages and voltages. Serve your dog this tray and he will only eat what he needs. He intuitively understands what is best for him.

An important contraindication with pregnant dams is to be careful not to work near their hocks or around the Conception Vessel. There have been reports of spontaneous aborts. During pregnancy, it is better to err on the side of caution. Work only the Yang meridians on the dorsal and lateral aspects of her body.

There are no contraindications for off-the-body work.

Staying gentle and staying out of your dog's way, allows him/her to control the session. Have we mentioned that it is the dog's massage?

**Exercise 21**
**Positional release on acupoints**

Practice using the positional release techniques on acupoints and meridians. Place your hands gently on your dog's body, with one hand above and the other below a particular acupoint. Without actually moving them, visualize your hands holding a tiny bit of tension as the energy between them moves apart, together, stretches, or compresses. Allow your imagination, in-out-around, circling in one direction, then reversing, flowing with the movement until you sense balance.

Work the segments on a meridian in the same way, expanding the length of the segments and sensing the flow from one hand to the other.

# Unit 6
# Auras and Chakras

Chapter 22
Auras, Energy Shells and Chakras

The energetic body is the field of flowing energy that overlays and extends beyond the physical we can see and touch. It has powerful and potent aspects. The energy that makes up your dogs body is not static. It is fluid in its movement. It can stay small and compact, residing within a single cell or it can expand as far as the range of emotional imagination (ROE) can go. It flows in and out, through and around the body. Both inside and outside the body, the energy is Ch'i. Ch'i permeates all things animate and inanimate. "It is also known as the Universal Energy Field." [Brennan]

The area around the body is a continuation of the body, albeit in a less dense form. Barbara Brennan describes in the book, *Hands of Light*, that there are several shells around the body, which represent physical, emotional –short term and long term. These are filters through which we perceive and interact with our surroundings and the people and animals in them.

Auras, Energy shells and Chakras are all ways of explaining the same phenomena. The complete picture of the fields around the body is called the aura. The aura is divided into layers.

You can observe the feeling of the balance of your energetic body in a physical way. During meditation, T'ai Ch'i play or Ch'i Gung exercise, when you focus on the movements of your breath, you can create the sense of centeredness in your body. When you do this, you are connecting your physical to your energetic; your intellectual to your inner awareness. Even the sense of grounding that you feel when you are connected to the earth is an extension of this energy field.

The 3 lower layers, or shells, starting with the one closest to the body are The *Etheric Double*, the *Emotional* state and the *Mental* state. Each layer appears (feels) different and has a specific function. Each layer is associated with a chakra.

Level 1: The etheric double, the layer that is the

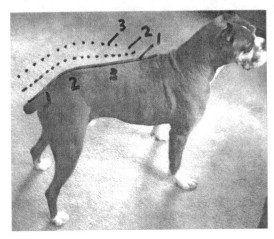

closest to the body, reflects the physicality of the body. It is associated with the Base Chakra.

*The 3 lower layers*

Level 2: The emotional shell is the next layer. It represents long held emotional and physical patterns such as abuse, abandonment, torture, and chronic diseases such as cancer, diabetes, etc. It is associated with the Sexual Chakra.

Level 3: The mental state is the 3rd layer. It represents more recent influences such as aromas, hunger, temporary anger, need to toilet, headache, irritability and sluggishness due to heaviness of atmospheric pressure. It is associated with the Solar Plexus (Stomach) Chakra.

These layers are palpable and accessible. These are the lower three layers of the spirit body. We can intentionally access and balance these fields any and every time we choose to. When was the last time you consciously touched the spirit of life, your dog's God-stuff?

On my recent birthday, a good friend of mine called me to congratulate me on the anniversary of the day that God came down to become me. I like that thought.
I wish the same to you and your dog on your special days. --JR

These are just the first three of at least eight layers on your dog.

So, what's a chakra, anyway?

Chakras have been described and experienced on a number of levels and in a number of ways. They have been called "energy vortices," (pleural of vortex) swirling funnel shaped (like little tornados) access points on specific points on the body. The shapes and sizes of these energy swirls create the aura.

Chakra / Energy balancing
Your dog's body is self-regulating, but sometimes it needs support and direction.

*Funnel shaped "energy vortices swirling on specific points on the body.*

The chakras are an energy system that comes into the body through the crown, top of the head, and goes to the base of the spine. Within this system are 8 major chakras and many minor chakras. They have also been described as wheels of energy continually opening and closing like the petals of a flower.

> Chakras are formed by the way dogs think, feel and handle life situations

Balanced chakras are approximately 4-6 inches in diameter and swirl in either a clockwise or counterclockwise direction.

> Your dog's life condition can be seen by observing Chakras.

Chakras are formed by the way dogs think, feel and handle life situations. This includes their current situations as well as long-term issues. "We are what we think," also applies to dogs. The chakras are seen by observing your dog's life condition. We cannot see the wind and yet we know it is there by the breeze against our faces. We did not see the dog mess yet we know its essence in the treads of our shoes.

We usually think of chakras as a line of vortices, 1-8. They can also be revealed as energy shells around the body.

*Chakras as a line of vortices, 1-8 with lines at skeletal transitions*

8
7
*Chakras as* 6
*energy shells* 5
4

They are also 3
the layers of 2
the aura. So 1
the first layer
would be the
Base Chakra,
the second layer,
the sexual, and
so on. Each
is influenced and

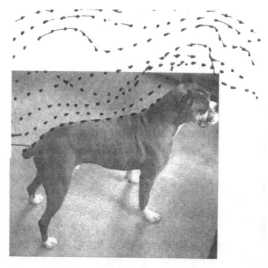

influences all the other chakras. The layers that domin-
ate are the ones that determine his life condition, how
he feels, and how he feels about himself.

All the chakras are there, some of them are more
apparent than the others. (See "Filters," Chapter 25)
An easy way to remember and locate the chakras is to
think of the skeleton of the dog. Where the bones
change shapes and directions are called transition
points (where they change from one shape and form to
another).

Major Chakras are located at skeletal transitions.
Soft tissue of nose to Muzzle
Muzzle to skull
Back of skull to cervical
Cervical to thoracic
Thoracic to lumbar
Lumbar to sacral
Sacral to tail

These are the locations of the chakras. The energy
you are working with is fluid and dynamic. As with all
energy points, they are constantly moving, opening

and closing, ebbing and flowing, in and out of balance and harmony. Don't expect them to always be in the same exact spot each time, even on the same dog. Chakras reveal the current moment-to-moment life condition.

Your dog's life condition changes from moment to moment, from thought to thought. His entire concepts of the comfortable vs. uncomfortable, fair vs. unfair, and heaven and hell are dramatically different before and after he has eaten and/or been let out to pee.

## Use of the Pendulum

The best initial way to experience locations and movements of chakras is by observing their patterns and strengths of their movements. The movement of a pendulum, any small weight suspended on a string or chain held over each of the chakra locations, can determine their movements, directions, forces and vitality. You can see their movements by watching their "wake," through the energetic body.

Pendulums don't need to be pricey artifacts from New Age shops. Anything that can be suspended and freely mobile will work. We have used pendants on necklace chains (diamonds work great), crystals on leather strings, and cork bottle tops, attached to a thread with a simple sewing needle.

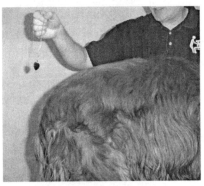

Pendulums are often put in the same chakra category as

*Pendulum over 1ˢᵗ, or base*

Ouija boards and other woo-woo stuff. The use of pendulums, like muscle testing, which is also growing in acceptance, is a way for us to bypass the intellectual part of our minds to connect with the wisdom of our unconscious, our spirit. Like the Ouija, pendulum work utilizes the connection of the energies of the observer and the observed. This connection is the same body-spirit intelligence that we are accessing through acupressure and the follow-on of positional release.

> The pendulum connects to the same body-spirit intelligence that we access through acupressure and the follow-on of positional release.

Holding the cord of your pendulum as still as possible with its weight suspended, you will notice that it will remain quiet when it is away from the body. It will only begin to move when it is held over a high-energy area, i.e., your dog's chakra. The pendulum moves in the wake of the movement of energy You will note there is no movement unless you are directly over a chakra vortex. Movement identifies the locations of Chakras.

*Each vortex swings in the next opposite direction.*

You can see the direction of energy wakes. direction that the pendulum swings shows its relationship to adjacent chakras. You can also tell by the character of the movement if the chakra is in balance, is disconnected from or overwhelmed by other chakras' energy.

When in balance, each vortex will swing in the opposite direction from the next. It resembles the movement of cogs in old clock wheels. Each cog redirects the action of the next cog.

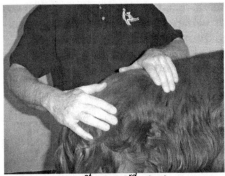

*Connecting 1ˢᵗ and 3ʳᵈ chakras*

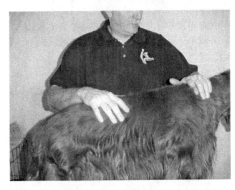

*Connecting 3rd and 5th chakras*

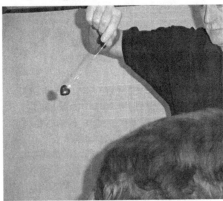

*Assess with your pendulum*

The vitality and the shape of the swing determine the quality of the chakra, round as opposed to oval or back and forth in one plane. Strong decisive, circular movement indicates vitality. Weak, oval, back and forth, or erratic patterns indicate lack of vitality, stagnation, or disconnection.

If your pendulum is not changing directions, the chakras are out of balance with each other and need to be realigned. You can realign them. Reinforce the like-moving movements of vortices, connecting the first to the third, the third to fifth, and the fifth to the seventh.

Then, connect the other like moving vortices, the second to the fourth, the fourth to sixth and sixth to the eighth. Reassess to see if the chakras are now balanced and realigned. This is usually all that needs to be done.

**Exercise 22**
**Pendulum**

Your dog can be standing, sitting or recumbent. Holding your hand as steady as possible, suspend the pendulum over each of the chakra areas.

- Observe the quality of the movements of the pendulum as you come nearer, are directly over and move away from each chakra.
- Note the directions of each of the chakra's swirls.
- Note that the force or lack of movement of one chakra will influence the others.
- The dog is a continuum of flowing energy. Bring the pendulum 6-10 inches further from your dog's body.
- Note any difference in the character of the movements of the pendulum.

Chapter 23
Chakras and Applications of Chakra Information

Okay, so now you know what chakras are, where they are located, how to find them, and how they move. What do they represent? And, what can you do with this information?

Chakras connect to emotional and physical states in and around your dog's body. Each chakra represents a specific area of his body. So, each chakra can be used to assess each of the aspects of his life condition, or quality of life, at each point. Chakra energy is also influenced with sound, color or vibration.

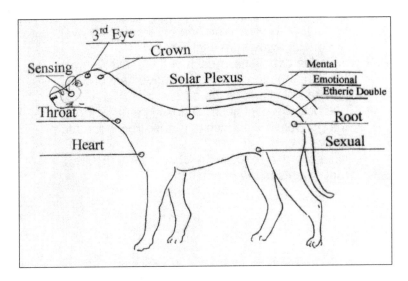

The following chart shows the location, the (English) name of the chakra, the color that is associated with it, the musical note that is sympathetic with its vibration, the gland that is associated with its functioning and the parts of the emotional life that would be affected by it.

**Frequency**

| NAME | COLOR | NOTE | GLAND/HORMONE | EFFECTS |
|------|-------|------|---------------|---------|
| 1. Root | Red | C | Gonad | Basic instincts |
| 2. Sexual | Orange | D | Pancreas | Prime directive: Reproduce/procreation |
| 3. Solar Plexus | Yellow | E | Adrenal | Place in pack, fear: Transition |
| 4. Heart | Green or Rose | F# | Thymus | Seat of inner knowing, confidence |
| 5. Throat | Blue | G | Thyroid | Vocalize. Overt barking, kennel cough |
| 6. Sensory | Purple | A | Jacobsen's organ | Viewing outside world |
| 7. 3rd Eye | Indigo | B | Pineal | How they see themselves |
| 8. Crown | Violet | C | Pituitary | Relationship to top dog owner/handler |

Chakras are at transition points on the skeleton:
Beginning of Muzzle
Muzzle to skull,
Cranium to Occipital Bone
Back of skull to cervical,
Cervical to thoracic,
Thoracic to lumbar,
Lumbar to sacral,
Sacral to tail.

Chakras also follow the major glands/hormone producing areas:
Pituitary
Pineal
Jacobsen's organ
Thyroid
Thymus
Adrenal
Pancreas
Gonad

## Three Lower Chakras

Your dog's three lower chakras represent his connection to the earth, his instinctual -- primal conditions. His instinctual concerns are with stability (grounding), propagation (sexuality) and safety (fear). These are located in the Root Chakra, the Sexual Chakra, and the Solar Plexus Chakra. All three are located on the lower part of the dog's body and refer to lower, more instinct driven processes. Get these coordinated with each other and you have set a firm foundation.

The *Root* is the bottom or first chakra. It is at the seat, closest to the ground when seated. When standing, it is closest to the base of the sacrum. It is the point where spirit and matter come together.

When your dog sits, he is connecting his physical body, his butt, to the ground, the earth spirit. It is "grounding," connecting him to the "ground." The Root chakra is associated with the Etheric Double, the energy plane closest to the body and it reflects what is happening within his physical body.

The Root chakra is affected by deep fears and anger. It is the "will to be" in the physical. It represents the functions of maintaining basic instincts of protection and the will for personal survival and propagation of the species.

The root chakra affects the adrenal glands, the kidneys, the urinary bladder and the spine. It resonates with the color red and the vibration of the tone of "C". The Root chakra is the reference level of congenital disease (Source Ch'i).

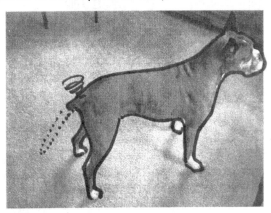

*Root Chakra, Number1*

Application 1.
If you were working with a puppy who was the runt of a litter, who lacks the will to survive, this would be the chakra that you could well focus on. You know that the Root chakra represents congenital issues. Some of these may be emotional conditioning that begins *prior* to birth.

Application 2.
You assess the chakra with a pendulum, or if you are more adept, with your hand. If you sense that it is out of alignment with other chakras, feeling too strong or too weak. You bring your dog's attention to the chakra to initiate his internal healing. Using the information in the chart, you have him lie on a red (color/vibration enhancing) pillow or blanket. You use a light with a red filter, so he could experience the red frequencies of light. You have a chime or bell that is tuned to the note C that you play in the dog's presence.

With the understanding of what the Root chakra represents, you have more insight into why your dog may be a fear-biter and/or apprehensive about any movement around his rear end. If he or she is sensitive in this area, there are emotional issues that need to be addressed. His spiritual issues can be addressed through work on the body.

Connecting and grounding is important for all dogs, so you would always acknowledge and honor this chakra during each massage session.

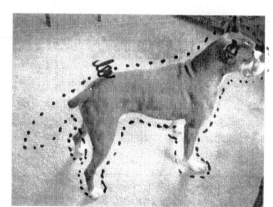

*Sexual Chakra, Number 2*

The second chakra is called the *sexual* chakra. Its layer is the Emotional shell. It has the function governing self-esteem, acceptance of self-responsibility, sexuality and relation-ships. This is the description for humans. It also applies to dogs. Its color is Orange. Its tone is D.

It is also his connection to the earth. The prime directive for all living organisms is to reproduce to maintain the species. It is located in the sex Organs— the gonads and controls the reproductive system, the lower back area, hips, legs and feet. As such, it is the ability to maintain forward movement in life.

The second chakra is accessed if your dog is in the breeding or whelping process, has just been neutered or spayed and/or is readjusting hormonal balances. As dogs age, their hormone production changes. When other dogs sense that their performance has declined, their position in their pack will be likely to be challenged. The $2^{nd}$ Chakra supports their pack status.

Application 3.
Your dog has just been neutered. He has just returned from his vet's office and his anesthetic is still wearing off. His hormones are out of balance. His level of testosterone that had been produced by his gonads has suddenly stopped, shocking his system. Assess his second chakra's vitality, shape and movement. Connect it with the fourth, sixth and eighth chakras for support and reinforcement. Place him on an orange pad or use orange or full spectrum lighting. Support him with the D tone.

Dog aggression or over submissiveness are examples of behavior when the second chakra is out of balance. When you want to complement and enhance behavioral modification training, it is important to access and balance this chakra.

Application 4.
You reach down to pet your dog and he rolls over onto his back and urinates. This indicates an imbalance in his sexual chakra. His disconnect with grounding, his $1^{st}$ chakra, and with his control over fear issues, $3^{rd}$ chakra, is manifested in his $2^{nd}$, sexual chakra.

The *Solar Plexus* Chakra is the 3$^{rd}$ layer, the mental state. It is located just above and two inches behind the umbilicus, directly over the stomach. The color is Yellow, tone is E, and function is to know the place in the hierarchy of the pack.

This chakra controls the functions of the pancreas, the stomach and the liver. The stomach is where that knot in the gut is felt when you experience dread. It is the place where we perceive fear. When a dog doesn't know what to expect, he experiences a twisting in the stomach, just like humans.

*Solar Plexus Chakra, Number 3*

Dogs crave routine. They want the same foods, the same activities, the same sounds and their same people. When their worlds are upset, they feel it in their stomachs. Bloating, cramping, diarrhea, and going off feed are behaviors associated with fear – of not knowing what to expect. These are examples of the relationships of emotions, digestion and bloat.

The Solar Plexus chakra is the highest of the lower three chakras and the transition to higher levels of understanding and consciousness. The third chakra connects your dog's instincts to his unconscious emotions. It is over activated with fear and emotional over reaction. Once this chakra is balanced, your dog will be free to focus on higher creativity such as learning, refining skills, bonding and playing with you.

Each of the linear chakras has a layer that corresponds to it. There are 5 more chakras that coincide with the layers and their emotion elements.

> The layers of chakras can be seen by observing your dog's life condition.

Whichever aspect of the life condition that is most present is the one you will see, or access. Recall that the aura, the layers of chakras can be seen by observing your dog's life condition. This brings us to the long-term beliefs, or emotional holding patterns in our dogs.

The **first chakra is associated with long-term beliefs and conditions.** This includes congenital issues, prenatal and bred-in behavioral characteristics.

The **second chakra represents emotional holding patterns** as a result of dogs' life experiences and training. These include relationships with their mother and other puppies in their litter, very early training and any remembered abuse that they might have received or perceived.

The **third chakra connects with more recent influences,** such as, the time of day (circadian rhythm), barometric pressure, noises, temperature, current health condition, hunger, anger, and loneliness. These are all temporary states that dogs deal with all the time.

The **fourth chakra represents the heart** and the actions of the heart. In ancient times, the heart was considered to be the place in our bodies where thought originated. In ancient Egypt, carved stone containers were used to store all the essential organs that would be needed by an embalmed pharaoh in the afterworld. Separate urns would contain the liver, the heart, the kidneys, etc.; except the brain, which they scooped out and discarded, since it didn't resemble anything else in the body. The heart did all the thinking and feeling. Today, we recognize that the heart is the site of your dog's seat of inner knowing and confidence. It represents wisdom and courage. It takes wisdom and sometimes courage to control the lower three chakras.

The **fifth chakra represents the throat**, or speech. This controls your dog's ability to communicate to other dogs and to us. With the throat chakra he discusses the wisdom of his decisions made through his lower four chakras. With dogs, this chakra refers to his ability and willingness to communicate. It includes verbal as well as nonverbal communication of body language and sending telepathic messages.

The **sixth chakra is unique to non-humans**. It is located in the muzzle and represents their connection to their perceived world. It collects and registers tastes, smells, pressures, magnetic attractions, sights, and more. It is where the dog connects with his environment; how he comprehends his outside world.

The **seventh is the third eye**, or Upper Dan Tian. This is their inner vision; dogs ability to see themselves as they are in their life condition. This would equate to your dog knowing his place in his pack and his physical and emotional state.

The **eighth chakra,** for humans, is our connection to our higher power, or our personal interpretation of God. Dogs do not appear to have an organized form of religion with written texts, rules and dogmas. (Yes, you read *dog-ma*!) They do know their place in their social order, though. The eighth chakra represents connection with the highest power they can imagine. That would be you, their master.

Summary

- Chakras relate to specific organs, organ systems and emotional patterns.
- The strength or weakness of the chakra indicates the wellness of that particular aspect of the dog.
- Chakras are formed by the way dogs perceive and handle their life situations.
- Chakras reflect your dog's life condition.
- Chakras are fluid.
- Chakras change with the time of day, his sense of safety, with each thought.

## Exercise 23
## Sensing energy fields

Rub the palms of your hands together, creating warmth from the friction.

Press your palms together, feeling the heat build between them. Slowly pull them apart and hold them shoulder width apart with palms facing the dog. Slowly scan the area above the dog's body with your hands, starting at the top of the head and moving, on either side of the spine, down his back to the tail. Make several passes, the first ones about 1 inch above the coat, then 4 to 6 inches above the coat and others around foot above.

Your hands will intuitively seek out and locate the correct levels. Observe your sensations in the bases of your palms. Do you feel warmth, coolness, vibrations, tingling, thickness, thinness, and/or variations in the resistance patterns? Do you sense them moving in circles or patterns? Observe these sensations at varying distances from the dog.

If you feel nothing, refocus on your breathing and try again. This is a skill that develops with time, patience and letting go of expectations. One cannot force it to happen. Observing how your hands move over your dog's body is a good way to start.

Chapter 24
Reality Check

You wave your hands over your dog's body. What's going on? What does a chakra layer feel like? Is it warmer or cooler? Is it like an air current? Some people say they can see auras; what do they mean? Which chakra are you influencing? What if you are in the wrong layer? Can you harm your dog by stimulating the wrong layer? Why are we learning all this stuff about chakras, anyway? Where are my dogs? I think I hear them calling me to take them out for a walk. We need some fresh air!

These are all normal, natural thoughts. You are not alone.

What may look like waving your hands over the dog is actually, with intention and experience, a way to assess your dog's energy fields. Once your hands and sensibilities are more aware, you can feel movement, direction, weakness, strengths, heat and coolness. You will detect ripples in the air pressure; areas around his body of flow and areas of stagnation. The energy vortexes of the Chakras will be felt, assessed, balanced and coordinated with the rest of the chakras. Many emotional issues that your dog holds in his aura eventually will show up as discomfort or disease in his physical body. But, by accessing them in his astral body, before they manifest as observable symptoms, they can be resolved. And, moving from the other direction, physical symptoms can often be resolved through work in the astral planes, the auric body. The mind and spirit affect the body; and the body affects the mind and spirit.

What does a chakra layer feel like?

There is an exercise that will help to demonstrate the feeling of the layers. Rub your hands together – creating friction – press your palms together then pull them 1" apart and feel the connection. Slowly compress the space between the hands. The resistance you feel is what an edge of the layer in the aura feels like.

You can also hold your hands over a chakra site; sensing the circular movement of its wake. Move slowly, assessing, from the base of the tail to the head. Connect to one vortex with one hand and identify another vortex with your other hand. Place your hands above them. Sense the connection between them. Sense if they are of similar strength, direction and shape.

Here are some experiences that describes energy work:

---

**Gant**

One very cold Christmas eve, several years ago, I got a call from the owners of the barn where I was boarding my horse, Gant [short for "Elegant"], a beautiful, high-strung, flashy Arab gelding, bay with black mane and tail and 4 white socks. He had foundered (the only time) and they wanted to know what I thought they should do. They had already tried several vets and all were too busy to come out to the barn. I asked them to keep him moving and I would be there, ASAP.

Forty-five minutes of slippery, frantic driving later, I pulled into their driveway. When I entered the barn, I saw Gant, propped up against the wall in his stall with two small, tired women holding him up. He was covered with dust and straw, his eyes were dull and his head looked heavy. He was in a funk. I looked at him and felt a wave of nausea flow over me. My tongue and throat were sticky-thick and my stomach churned in empathy.

We pulled him out into the center of the aisle and the two held him steady. The barn was unheated. It was a long 60-stall building with 30 stalls on each side of a wide cement aisle. Bare light bulbs, suspended from the ceiling beams every 20 or so feet, dimly illuminated the area.

---

You could hear the sounds of the other horses in the aisle moving about in their stalls quietly slurping water and munching hay.

I scanned Gant with both hands, following the contours of his body 3 to 6 inches off the surface. At a point around his stomach, I sensed a distortion in his energy. I connected to this point with my hands and backed away feeling for the edge of his affected layer. I backed up and up until I was over 30 feet away from him. At this point I felt the edge of the shell. It was a knowing and a trusting that it was there. It felt like a soap bubble with no moisture. I held the "bubble," waiting for it to shift.

All of a sudden, we noticed that the barn was absolutely silent. The horses on both sides of the aisle had stopped moving and munching. The row of lights overhead flickered. We felt a surge of electricity move through the air. The "bubble" I was holding softened and just like that--was gone. Gant raised his head and looked toward me. His tail arched up and he let go a huge blast. He shook his head and neck and started prancing about on the cement. His color was back, his eyes were bright, and his attitude was back. Gant was back.

The two who witnessed this, one of whom was a true skeptic, an OR nurse, had never seen energetic healing work before. They had felt the electricity, too. They kept repeating, "If we hadn't seen it ourselves, we never would have believed it."

They called me several times after that to work with other horses.

You can see how we are combining and overlaying several concepts creating a unified theory. All are unique ways of expressing the similar ideas. You'll see, for example, that the 3$^{rd}$ energy layer and the Solar Plexus chakra are similar in concept to the Stomach Meridian, and the Limbic System.

Many energywork practitioners maintain that they can see the colors and patterns of the layers of chakras (Brennan, *Hands of Light*). Open yourself to the possibility that you can see colors. Once you've seen them, your life will never be the same. What colors fill your field of vision? When you soften your vision and look to the edge of your dog's body, you may see subtle outlines or shapes. This is his *subtle body*. *Colors* also identify Chakras.

The level of the Chakra is determined by the life condition of the dog. Whatever presence you sense is what your dog has chosen to work on at some subconscious or subcutaneous level. It is entirely up to the mystical workings of the dog. You cannot control your dog's healing dynamics. It is his responsibility; his job, his session. If you feel you must control the event, your ego is getting in the way. When ego, or your mind starts trying to control, then it is virtually impossible for you to just be present to witness your dog's session. Is it your session, or your dog's?

## Weimaraner

I was demonstrating PetMassage$_{TM}$ at a dog show offering 5 or 10-minute sessions. A magnificent young Weimaraner dog was brought to our massage booth for a session. He was agitated and highly unfocused, different from the excited exuberance normal to the breed.

The owner/handler said that the dog was in an automobile accident at the previous week's dog show and had been trapped in the back of a van for over two hours. Paramedics were called to crack open the van to extricate him, using their Jaws of Life. The crash had showered him with broken glass. He was frightened but checked out to be physically okay. He was also reacting to his owners and handlers angst about the long term effects of the traumatic event. One of the worst things that can happen to them is to get the "scaredies."

His handler said he didn't think they were going to enter him that day. They just wanted him to be comfortable in the show environment and not connect it with the anxiety of the accident.

We lifted him onto the table. He spun and whirled without any acknowledgement of my (healing) presence.

I was intent on demonstrating the PetMassage$_{TM}$ techniques to the handlers. My ego was directing me to show just how terrific our techniques are and how they'd be able to help their dogs with them. I thought, "That's why they are paying me." I struggled with the dog; pulling and holding, reaching and straining just to keep him from bounding off the massage table.

In a flash, I was reminded what my real purpose was... to help the dog. It wasn't to prove how skilled and knowledgeable I am.

I remembered that it wasn't my massage and it wasn't the handlers' massage. It was the dog's massage. I had been fighting with the dog for 4 minutes of the 5-minutes session and neither of us was benefiting. We were both becoming more and more upset and frustrated. I sensed that what he needed most was to feel centered and grounded. It was certainly what I needed at this point.

I placed one hand on his throatlatch and the other on his croup. I closed my eyes and centered myself by observing my breath as I slowly inhaled and exhaled a couple of times. I opened one eye. The dog was standing amazingly still. His head was turned toward me. His eyes focused on my face. He had been searching for a quiet place, too.

I completed his session with some long, slow grounding strokes over his topline and down each of his legs, to physically and emotionally reconnect him to the earth. Then, he was led away. I silently thanked *him* for the lesson.

A couple of hours later, I saw him returning to our booth with his ecstatic owner and handler. They had decided to enter him in the show after all. He had just won Best of Breed!

There are two lessons here:
1) It's the dog's massage, not ours.
2) Intention, love and staying on purpose can create a safe place for the dog paralyzed by fear.

Is it possible to harm your dog? Yes:

These are more contraindications for your massage:

1) if you are to rough

2) if you are forcing the session or

3) if you are not reacting to your dog's needs. Your dog know his body

You will find that you will be called to work with dogs that are in pain; who have just had an injury, accident or surgery.

If your touch is hurting your dog, he will lick the painful spot, turn to look at you or move away from the pain. If his subtle cues don't get your attention, he may snap at your hand or bite. One way or another, he will let you know his boundaries.

Dogs usually intuitively know what is best for them. They will only accept as much as they can handle. When they are complete with the amount of massage they can use, they will let you know. They will sit down,

go to sleep or simply leave. They have no need for pretence. When they are done, they're done.

Once you have an understanding and working knowledge of these concepts more magnificent and awesome experiences than you can imagine will open to you.

You will be able to facilitate healings, transitions and affect behavioral dysfunctions in positive ways. The physical body is wondrous in its design and functioning. Combine that with the wonder of its emotional, spiritual, and astral planes, including past and future life experiences, and well, your universe will have no limits. Your dog's universe will be enlightened, too. It shouldn't be necessary to dress him in saffron robes for his walks, though. He's still your ol' dog-buddy. He's just happier and more at peace with himself and his environment.

**Exercise 24**
**Ruffles have ridges**
**Sensing the ruffles in the energy field.**

Rub the palms of your hands together, creating warmth from the friction. When you feel the warmth build, press them together. Be aware of the pressure and the stillness. Slowly pull them apart, creating a ball of energy. Direct your palms toward the dog, holding them shoulder width apart. Keeping your wrists and hands supple, make several slow passes from head to tail above the dog, the first ones about 4 to 6 inches above the coat.

Set your hands in front of your shoulders. Movement of your arms and hands across the topline of your dog happens by shifting your weight from one foot to the other, not by moving your arms across your body. Feel the difference between moving your arms from your chest (pectoral) muscles as opposed to drawing power from the movements of your legs. Each movement starts from and is an extension of, the power deep within the earth.

Observe any sensations in the bases of your palms. Your hands will intuitively seek out and locate the correct level. When you sense ripples in the air, visualize them as tangles in a horses main and comb through them, pulling with your curved, spread fingers.

Keep breathing and rhythmically transferring your body weight from one foot to the other.

Make several passes through the resistance, until you feel your hands moving through smoothly and effortlessly. You have just combed through a ruffled energy field and assisted your dog in detangling -- reprogramming the patterns in his energy shells that are affecting and reflecting his quality of life. This is called unruffling.

Chapter 25
Filters

A filter is the veil or sieve through which perceptions are interpreted. An example of a filter for people would be sunglasses. Without eye protection in bright sunlight, you have to deal with brightness, glare, sneezing and discomfort. The effects that the light has on your eyes, affects your comfort and your mood. It affects your emotional brain, your Limbic system. Your mood variations can be dramatic. Lens colors of blue and gray cool and darken your vision; amber and yellow warm by enhancing colors and making the red tones pop. Our dogs' quality of life experience is determined by the way they perceive their relationships between themselves and the outside world.

We usually think of perceiving our world through our five senses: seeing, hearing, smelling, touching and tasting. Roger Caras, the noted naturalist, has written that he believed dogs might have as many as twenty, some of which we haven't even imagined!

The major filters through which a dog interprets and relates to himself and his environment are similar to those of people:
- Satiety, hungry or not as hungry
- Temperature, hot or cold
- Hydration, moist or dry
- Dog's perception of his abilities to perform Activities of Daily Living, ADL's - limitations he puts on himself
- Chronic or acute pain and/or lameness
- Disease
- Traumas and dismemberment due to surgeries and injuries
- Past or present abuse, whether perceived or real, both are equally destructive to your dog's psyche
- Loneliness

- Anxiety
- Fear
- Grief
- Uncertainty of social status, placement in pack hierarchy
- Hormones i.e. testosterone, insulin, endorphins.

Mood is a powerful filter for both people and dogs. When you have joy in your heart you can walk outside on a cold rainy day and you'll enjoy yourself; but if you are in a state of rage, whatever you do, wherever you go and whomever you meet, no matter how beautiful the weather, will be unpleasant. Wherever we go, we take ourselves with us. Our and our dog's whole outlook on life is shaded by our experiences and our burdens of unhappiness and heavy memories.

**Emotional state**
Dogs have mood changes. They can be cranky, silly, bored, angry, confused, arrogant, etc. And dogs are extremely empathetic too. This means they not only have their own moods, they also get to experience the moods of others. Your mood swings are picked up, processed and experienced by your dog. This is especially true during a massage when your dog allows himself to be even more vulnerable and open. Through touch, you both experience the immediate connection and powerful transference of energy, thought and spirit. Your dog is working with and through you.

Remember that your dog's mind is following on the inside wherever your touch is on the outside. He follows the depth of pressure, the direction, and intention. If extraneous emotions and thoughts cloud your intentions, he will respond to them as if the issues were his own.

Ground and focus yourself before each massage. During the session, as soon as you notice that your mind is wandering, refocus. If you sense that your dog is becoming distracted and less responsive to your touch, check in with yourself, he may be responding to your private distractions.

When you let him, your dog will guide your hands, showing you where his attention is needed the most. This is as much a part of the dog's body language as pointing to a spot with his nose, sniffing or scratching at an area, or moving his body into your hands.

Distraction is a major filter. We are all easily distracted. * But for dogs, their job description is to be vigilant, constantly aware of their surroundings. In other words, they are hardwired for paying attention to distractions. Reduce distractions for yourself and your dog as much as you can by becoming aware of and limiting discordant music, noises, other pets, TV, non-participating people, children, cooking aromas, scented candles, incense and colognes.

Do you need to create a sterile environment? No, but your dog will surely be more comfortable where there is less stimulation. Ideally, we would like to create an environment in which your dog can forget about the outside world and allow his own body to be the focus of his attention. This can only be done if you create an environment for you, where you can forget about the outside world. It could happen. Once you've contained your distractions, your dog will be able to easily empathize.

* See how easy that was? Now you can go on back to continue the paragraph.

## Scent

Your dog's olfactory abilities need to be taken into consideration. They are as much as 100 times more sensitive than ours. That's why they do the tracking and we follow them. We humans have the unique ability to turn off scents within a few seconds, to adapt to our environment. If, for example, we're near an oil refinery, or near nasty smelling garbage, we initially gag at the air quality, and gasp for breath. Within a minute, though, we've shut down our olfactory receptors and adapted. We can then breathe and talk and work and move on with our lives. Dogs do not have that luxury. Dogs do not appear to have this internal shut-off valve.

An important part of their job/life description is to be ever vigilant, aware of all the odors around them, their strengths, variations, locations and any other information they can use. If you use *aromatherapy,* be aware that the intensity of the fragrance may be overwhelming to your dog and may be so distracting he may not be able to focus on his own healing.

## Walter

Walter is a young Golden Retriever who had cruciate surgery, which left one of his hind legs weaker, with less muscle tone and volume than the other. After just one session, whenever I would sit in my little tripod stool and hold my hands in front of me, he would back into my hands so that we could focus our combined attentions to his hamstrings.

One session, Walter's mind was always busy. Whenever he felt maxed out with stimulation, he would get up and wander around. Then when he was ready for more work, he would return to sit back into my hands again.

One visit, Walter walked away from me and wandered into the kitchen. He came right back with a cold French fry from the garbage pail sticking out of his mouth. He sat back into my hands and quietly munched on his snack. Walter is a great teacher. I learned patience and the need to turn over the control of the session to the dog. The lesson is that it is the dog's massage, not mine.

During one of our workshops, our boxer, Oskar, was receiving a session as part of one our student's final return-demonstrations. Oskar is our "demo dog." He is experienced. He's been my teaching assistant for trade shows, seminars and over a hundred workshops. He is a pro. Our 4-month-old Standard Poodle, Jacques-o, decided that taunting him would be a fun game. Oskar stood on the table, watching as Jacques-o dropped tennis balls and other toys on the floor around the table and then *on* the table. He'd then pounce up and down into his play poses.

Oskar, the veteran of so many workshops, tried valiantly to stay focused on his job. We watched for several anguished minutes as his eyes crossed and his ears twitched in circles. When he could contain himself no longer, he exploded off the table after the grinning puppy. As he flew off after Jacques, his kick was so forceful he knocked over the table and the laughing student.

I made house calls to the home of an ancient little dog who was suffering the effects of age, arthritis and a lifetime of Toy Poodledom. Stiffness, soreness, weakness, crunching leg joints and irritability made up the stuff of this little guy's everyday life. His family loved him so. He was *never* "allowed on the furniture." But, since he had been getting on the furniture every day whenever they weren't home for over 14 years anyway, whenever they would leave him home, they created steps with sofa pillows so their mischievous poodle's life would be a little easier.

These visits were exercises in distraction. The living room where she received her session had the TV, which was turned on. Dinner was cooking and the aromas were delicious. Curious neighbors poked their heads through the front door to ask if they could watch. The only distractions that were missing were kids and other pets.

Having other dogs in the room while you are working is okay, as long as they are not distracting.

Memories are embedded in our bodies. They are stored and accessed from not only the gray matter in dogs' skulls, but throughout their bodies, in their bones, muscles, and other tissues. These memories are stimulated as our hands move on and around your dog's body. We don't need to know the content of the memories, just as we don't need to know what our dogs are chasing in their sleep as their legs kick, tails and lips twitch.

*Holding patterns* are emotional, behavioral or physical habits that have become part of your dog's nature. They can be positive, as in his proud head carriage and happy, prancing front legs that he displays when he carries his leash in his mouth. Or, they could be the clever stylistic way he balances his weight on his back paws while defecating. They can also be negative. Consider destructive behavior during thunderstorms, separation anxiety, fear biting, food aggression and barking at the uniformed people.

His fears and anxieties all developed from unpleasant experiences. He may have started with certain personality traits, so he was bound to be good at some things and not as good at others. All habits had to have started sometime. They become part of your dog's personality and movement. The causative memories for the habits can be overwhelming, debilitating.

PetMassage$_{TM}$ Energy Work helps your dog access his conditioning, creating positive changes to affect the negative causes for his behavior.

Light and color effect dogs' life conditions dramatically. We've seen how the prismatic colors of the chakra wheel can influence dogs. See Chapter 44. Use of colored lights, filters and fabrics affect and correct Chakra imbalances. These are the colors of the rainbow. If you are unsure which color would be the most therapeutic, use 'em all. All of these frequencies are in sunlight and full spectrum lights.

One very effective tool is using the skill of visualization of color. Visualizing and projecting color onto an area of the dog's body that is out of balance or off-color is very supportive.

Dogs also can suffer from SAD, Seasonal Affective Disorder. Oskar finds any shaft of sunlight in the house and lays in it to counteract his winter depression. He moves across the room as the day progresses to stay in the light.

Location and arrangement is also important in establishing comfort. Students of Feng Shui understand that the placement of objects influences the levels, flows and activity of energy in an environment. Dogs are very sensitive not only to barometric pressures, lights, temperatures but magnetic and energetic influences as well. The size and shape of your room, the locations of windows, doors, mirrors, furniture and plants all affect how comfortable your dog feels and how willing he will be to participate in his session.

Once your dog is on your massage table, allow him to choose which direction he wants to face. The magnetic forces may not be noticeable to us, but may be the difference between comfort and struggle for your dog. Your dog has his own sense of Feng Shui. He knows which ways the best energetic winds blow. As your session progresses, he may get up and turn a different direction. That's fine. One of the defining characteristics of Ch'i is that it is not static, that it is constantly in motion. The energetic dynamics of the room may have altered with his internal (and your internal) evolution.

Sounds can be assistive or distracting. Several CD's of music and sounds specifically for animal massage are available. If you choose one of these, put yourself in your dogs place. Consider the distraction quotient in these recordings. Anything that has intrusive nature sounds, such as, birds, frogs, crickets, thunder or raindrops will draw your dog's attention away from his internal session. Rather than allowing his subconscious to take over, he'll be looking around, wondering, "Was that a cricket?" and "Where's that frog?"

Although your dog is surely the exception, most dogs do not appear to have well developed musical tastes. All of them respond to volume, pitch and rhythm, though. For some dogs, lower volume, deeper pitches and slower rhythms are calming. For others, higher pitches and faster rhythms are more sympathetic to their internal frequencies.

Most dogs appear to like the sound of human voices. So, if your preference is listening to talk radio or religious stations, your dogs will find musicality in it. Our horses used to draw comfort from country radio stations and the calm narrative voices delivering religious messages. Our dogs also like to listen to Click and Clack on the *Car Talk Show* on National Public Radio. If you find, while giving a massage session, that your thoughts are distracted by the intellectual content of the talk, switch to music.

**Basset Hound**
Each spring the Basset rescue group in
Birmingham, Michigan celebrates the breed with a
special day. Dogs and their people travel from all
over the country to participate in the "Basset
Waddle." The downtown of Birmingham is taken
over by a parade with fire trucks and clowns,
politicians and about a thousand hounds and their
owners, all howling and, well, waddling.  There is
a picnic where the dogs get to play with each
other. There are contests for best costume, the
furthest traveled, the oldest, and of course, the dog
with the longest ears.

At the starting point of the parade those of us who
were invited vendors set up our little booths to
market to and support all the people and dogs in
attendance. In our booth we were providing 5-
minute demo canine PetMassage$_{TM}$ sessions. I
was working nonstop as one Basset athlete after
another was hoisted onto the table for his or her
warm-up massage.  A fellow walked up to our
booth with his dog riding in an American Flyer
Wagon. The dog wore a bandana and had a shiny
cardboard New Year's hat on his head. His chin
rested on a pillow propped up against the sides of
the wagon.  The man told us that his dog had a
spinal injury and was paralyzed; he couldn't walk
or even move his head. They had traveled several
hundred miles for the parade. The dog didn't want
to miss it.

As I started my assessment strokes, scanning the
dog with my hands, I closed my eyes. I often close
my eyes to block out distractions. This time, as my

hand passed over the side of the dog's neck I noticed a small red dot in my field of vision. I held my hand over the neck, and watched, as the red spot grew larger and larger until it filled my field of vision. The intensity was as bright as looking at the sun through softly closed eyes.

I sensed that the throbbing red indicated raw pain. I wondered if I could change the image in my vision to a more soothing, healthful green.

A small square of green appeared in the middle of the red. Then another and another, until it was like a checkerboard. The red receded as the green squares continued to grow.

Soon the entire field was bright green. It took just a couple of minutes. I opened my eyes and saw the big brown eyes of the dog staring intently at me. I soon completed his PetMassage$_{TM}$ session. The man and his dog left for the parade and I turned to work with the next dog waiting in line.

An hour later, I heard a voice calling from the other side of the street. I looked up and saw the man waving at me, calling, "Thanks, Jonathan." The dog in the wagon lifted his head, looked at me and placed his head back on the pillow.

An hour later, I heard a voice calling from the other side of the street. I looked up and saw the man waving at me, calling, "Thanks, Jonathan." The dog in the wagon lifted his head, looked at me and placed his head back on the pillow.

The most important characteristic for any music you play is that it is comforting to you, the therapist. Your dog will empathize on your comfort level just as he responds to your thoughts. If you like Country, then that's the music you need to play. If you like Soft Jazz or Blues, that's what you, play. New Age music with its soft tones and minimalist structure is easy to work to for most of us. It allows our minds to become unfocused allowing our hands to flow with the actions of the dogs. Classical or hard-edged contemporary music may be too structured and controlling to allow your mind and spirit to float.

**Exercise 25**
**Dog's reaction to music styles**

Play several different styles of music. Observe your dog's reactions to the sounds. Compare his response to classical music, rock, jazz, new age, country, talk radio, excited, fast-paced programming, slow (religious stations), male voices, female voices, nature sounds.

Try not to let your tastes influence his reactions. In other words, during this exercise, try to abstain from singing along or dancing to your favorite numbers.

Test some other dogs to discover their musical preferences.

Compare big dogs to little dogs.
Compare old dogs to puppies or middle age dogs.

# Unit 7
# Essential Intangibles

Chapter 26
Healing Purpose and Intention

Why are you learning to massage dogs? Is it for the money? For the notoriety? To expand your client base (the money)? Would you rather work with animals than humans? Do you trust animals more than you do humans? Do you want to help dogs in their healing after they have experienced the traumas of accidents and surgeries? Do you want to comfort them during especially difficult bouts of pain from arthritis or disease? Do you want to help dogs work through their emotional stuff? Do you want to enhance your understanding about dogs and learn the lessons they have to teach us?

It is natural and instinctive to massage. When you bump your elbow, you don't have to think about it; you auto-matically put pressure on the sore spot. The first thing you do when you're hurt is to rub the area. When your tooth hurts, you hold pressure on it, right? PetMassage_TM techniques that we teach aren't new. They are part of our collective memory; *in* our collective memory, encoded in our DNA.

Massage intention can be directed toward the negative or the positive. Think of your massage as an "affirmative" session for your dog. You have the choice to focus your attention on disorder and disease, or order and health. If, as a massage therapist-instructor, your intention is to look for the trigger points and spasms in muscles, on a "search and destroy mission," you will find them. You can seek them out and eradicate them one by one, but after her session, your dog may feel that she has been through a battle...which she has.

Intention is a determination to act in a certain way to a preconceived final result. If your intention is to search for balance and wellness, you will find it. Anything that feels out of balance can be gently brought back into harmony with the rest of the body. Her resulting experience will be more peaceful and more oriented toward nurturing. The therapy will also last longer, since it is her body choosing its path rather than being forced. PetMassage$_{TM}$ Energy Work is gentle.

> Staying on purpose brightens your energy, enhancing it, magnifying it.

*Healing purpose* is very important in PetMassage$_{TM}$ energy work. This is our highest projected intention. *Intention* comes from your purpose, or reason for being and doing, your values of honesty, love and being authentic. It is connected with your Heart chakra. Your intention is part of your energetic body. You've already seen that the energetic body is a reflection of thoughts and sincerity. It connects and combines with your dog's energy. The quantity and quality of your connection will determine the kind of massage, the quality of your relationship and the type of healing that you both will experience. Dr. Wayne Dyer, the notable and quotable author, says, "When you change the way you look at things, the things you look at, change."

> It's the dog's massage,
> not ours.

> Intention = value, honesty,
> love and being real.

> Establish *intention* through communication
> with the dog.
> Intention comes from the place of being authentic.

Your connection to your intention is what you bring to the table. You are your intention. So, it is not so much what you do, it is what you *are*. You are the connection for your dog to Source. As your energy joins with your dog's, you create a synthesis. Whatever either of you brings to the relationship, whether positive, neutral or negative, affects the outcome. This all may sound very heavy and ponderous. Yet remember, and this is important, *PetMassage is fun.*

If you don't enjoy giving the massage, your dog won't be pleased with receiving it. You are doing everything you know exactly right. Release your expectations and simply enjoy your opportunity to share this quality time with your dog.

Keep the connection light, fun and loving. It will be healthful, therapeutic and joyful.

**Exercise 26**
**Touching wood**

Locate a small piece of wood, such as an 8-inch length of 2 x 4 or a stout, 1" thick branch. Sit quietly, observing your breath. Place your hands on the ends of the wood. Sense its continuing movement of life within its grain. Examine the ends, where it had been severed from a larger piece of wood. Sense its history, back to the tree, its sapling stage, the nut, its parent trees. Think of the birds and other wildlife that have had experiences with the tree. Feel your own energy as it flows through the wood from one hand to your other hand. Does the type of grain or condition of the wood affect your hand-to-hand energy flow?

Sometimes, when you feel disconnected, it is often enough to "touch wood," to help you become grounded.

Chapter 27
Principle of Entrainment

Entrainment is the paralleling of actions, movements, intentions, thoughts and emotions of client and therapist. It is often unconscious, i.e., yawning when someone else yawns, or when two people who are deep in conversation are seen leaning toward each other at a similar angle. When in agreement, happy in coordinating their thoughts and feelings, couple's strides and postures are similar; but when they disagree, their movement patterns move abruptly out of sync. It's interesting to watch mothers and their teen-age daughters walking together. At times they are in agreement and then, in a flash, one of them alters her stride. Children use their posture to be similar to or rail against their parents. This is called, *posturing*.

Entrainment extends to the emotional empathy that dogs feel for us. This is one of the reasons why therapy dogs are so effective in their visits to hospitals and nursing homes. They empathize emotionally with patients. They share the burdens of grief, hopelessness and pain. Dogs do not attach to the energy. They have the remarkable ability to allow energetic heaviness to slough off as they move on to the next eager patient with their wagging tails and wise, loving eyes. Every once in a while, you'll see them shake their whole body off the ground to physically slough off negativity and refresh themselves.

Entrainment goes both ways in PetMassage$_{TM}$. If your dog is nervous or anxious, you will be, too. If you are nervous or anxious, your dog will be, too. You are the only one who can have control over your own life. When you maintain your self-control (it's a good goal, anyway) you provide a solid platform for an easy, comfortable session with and for your dog.

Sometimes, your dog needs to connect with a "safe place." His primary intention may be that that is what he most needs to get from his PetMassage<sub>TM</sub> session. Recall the Weimaraner, who connected to his safe place. (See Chapter 24.)

He entrains with you. Give him permission to have self-control. Give him permission to have awareness of his healthy body.

**Exercise 27**
**Skin rolling over the spine**

Place both hands on either side of the spine, starting at the withers. Slowly, press your thumbs along side the spine, into the little indentations between the spinous processes of the vertebrae. Gather up on the coat into your palms with your fingers. Feel its elasticity as you pull it as far away from the body as you can. Then, when you sense its recoil, return it onto the body. Move back a hands-width along the spine and repeat. Stretch the coat, skin and fascia. Continue down the entire length of the spine to the base of the tail. Repeat at least three times.

Chapter 28
Love

Love is the cornerstone of work with animals. They are open vessels ready to receive your love; vessels filled with eagerness to share their love with you. When you love yourself, when your work comes from your loving spirit, you are more receptive and responsive in your connections with your dogs.

Sometimes your heart's not in your work. Sometimes, you would rather be somewhere else doing other things. Sometimes, your mind is occupied, taking care of other business. These are not the times to connect with your dogs. You must honor their spirits. You are asking them to be vulnerable and open, to entrain with your deeper resonance. Be aware of the quality of your own spirit that you are offering to them to access.

If you find that your mind is wandering, there are exercises you can do to Feng Shui your internal furniture. One is to put on a little Buddha smile, like the one on the faces of, well, *Buddha smile* Buddhist statuary. This will reprogram the rest of your body and spirit to be sweeter, happier, and more peaceful. This was one of the valuable lessons I learned from Amy Snow and Nancy Zidonis at their Tallgrass workshop.

Another, is to repeat out loud the laughing sounds of ho ho ho ho ho or ha ha ha ha ha or hee hee hee hee hee hee. Repeat any of these out loud 10 times and you *will* smile. Your smile will soften any hardness in your face and around your heart. Warmth radiates throughout your physical and energetic body. The warmth of your energy will envelope your dog in nurturing love.

### Exercise 28
### Laughing sounds

Repeat out loud, these laughing sounds, "Ho ho ho ho ho ho" and/or "Ha ha ha ha ha ha" and/or "Hee hee hee hee hee hee hee."

Repeat any or all of these out loud 10 times. Are you smiling yet?

# Unit 8
# Mechanics

Chapter 29
Body Mechanics

Your safety and comfort are dependent on how you and your dog move your bodies. For you to have your move-ments flow easily and smoothly, you must create and sustain ease and balance in your body. For your comfort, all your movements need to be natural and comfortable. You will both benefit from your good body mechanics.

At the PetMassage™ Institute, we have found that working with the dogs on tables is easiest for us. It saves us from crawling around after them. On a purely physical level, it protects our backs and knees from strain. Energetically, it takes the dogs off their home turf--the floor, so they relinquish a little of their control. Practically, it saves on wear and tear on the knees of pants.

When you reduce your dog's distractions he will cooperate more completely in his session. There will be fewer reasons for him to jump off the table, potentially hurting himself, or you, if you attempt to restrain him.

Your table needs to be solid and secure, with obvious edges, boundaries, so your dog will know where the table stops and the space around it begins. Once he feels the edge with his feet, he is less likely to jump or fall off.

*Your table needs to be solid and secure*

A table that is too soft with foam, such as a human massage table, will strain his shoulders and hips. It can cause hyperextensions in the hocks and carpals (front knees). You can lay a carpet over your table to make the surface firmer. This will also protect the table from claws. Make sure the table height is correct for you. A good way to check for correct table height is to stand in front of your table with your arms hanging comfortably in front of you. As you swing your arms, the backs of your knuckles should be lightly brushing the tabletop.

Dogs with severe arthritic conditions may not be comfortable being picked up. You may need to work on the floor with them and your larger dogs, that are too big or heavy to put on your table. Your floor surface needs to be non-skid so the dogs can feel the security of traction from their paws.

We also suggest that the area surrounding your table be carpeted or padded with firm material like 12" x 12" interlocking rubber mats. This will lessen the impact on his forelegs and shoulders if he should jump down. After your massage session, whenever possible, lift your dog and place him on the floor.

When helping your dog onto the table hold him close to your body, not out at arms length. When you rise from your squat, with your dog in your arms, stand straight up. LIFT WITH YOUR LEGS. If you are pulling up the dog at an angle, to hoist him onto your table, you may injure your back. When helping your dog off the table, again, hold him close to your body. Take a step away from the table and drop down into a squat so you can easily loose him onto the floor.

Often with a very large or heavy dog, you can get him to jump up by placing his front paws on the table. Then, it is an easy matter to hoist up his rear end. He will walk forward to accommodate you. Remember, when lifting his rear end, to LIFT WITH YOUR LEGS

Many dogs, when they feel they are complete in their session, or if they feel threatened, will leap off the table onto the floor. If they decide to bail, you have a couple of choices. You can restrain them to continue the session, which is indicated if they are (1) injured, (2) recovering from surgery, (3) temporarily distracted, or (4) having their first PetMassage$_{TM}$ experience and are unsure of why they are being touched. Or, you can let them jump.

Once they push off, do not try to catch them. Dogs are natural athletes and can easily make the transition from a two-foot table to the floor. They will not hurt themselves as long as you stay out of their way.

If you anticipate that your dog may snap or bite, he will sense your tightness and nervousness. He may envisage what you may be projecting: the image of the behavior that you are expecting. He may say to himself, "Okay, if that's what she wants, I won't disappoint her." Chomp!

> If you have any concerns whatsoever
> for your safety, instruct the owner of the dog
> and have her do the massage.

If the dog has a history of biting, is untrained or, has been trained to be fierce, have his owner or an assistant hold him or have him muzzled. If you have any concerns whatsoever for your safety, instruct the owner of the dog how to do the massage and have them touch their animal.

Your safety is of paramount importance. Sometimes dogs can be in so much pain and fear that they will refuse to give you their permission to touch them. Visualize how they are encasing themselves in protective energetic armoring. Their armor needs to be reduced and eliminated before you can make your connection. Honor their spaces. Maintain your patience and stay on purpose. Your dog will soon allow your hands near, with your energetic passes, then light touch and eventually, deeper massage.

> Armor needs to be reduced and eliminated before you can make your connection.

Whenever in doubt, focus on grounding yourself. This will help you stabilize your own energy by connecting with energy from the earth.

You may want to invest in steps for the dogs. This will save your back, reduce your dog's anxiety and save him from the discomfort of your putting unnecessary pressure on his sensitive bones and joints as he is being picked up. We have experimented with ramps and have found that not one of the dogs who used them, liked them. They know and understand steps. Moving up or down ramps appeared to be a confusing, and unfamiliar movement that was stressful to their joints.

While working on your dog, avoid over stretching your hands and arms. Visualize a straight line running from your forearm down your fore-finger…just like gripping a tennis racquet. Keep your hands in front of your shoulders. Do not allow your arms or hands to

*Good body mechanics makes Jocko smile*

cross in front of you. Crossing your arms in front of your body will constrict the muscles and fascia in your chest and, consequently, reduce the movement of air in and out of your lungs.

Continue to breathe comfortably and often We all have a tendency to hold our breath when in awkward or trying situations, and especially while learning new skills. Sometimes we just forget to breathe. Oxygen debt causes you to feel stressed, fatigued and confused.

All your movements in your massage start from your feet. Then your movements extend to become movement in your spinal column, your joints and pivot points. When you step, or plant your foot, your weight falls downward through the medial axis of your body to your feet. Your body can be compared to a coiled spring, which after absorbing the weight of your step, stores it and rebounds by releasing it again. Your breath is pulled into your body from below and your Ch'i is moved into all of the parts of your body. This is called breathing from the earth.

As in Tai Ch'i, each step flows into the next. In his book, *Embrace Tiger, Return to Mountain,* Al Huang writes, "When all imagery in your thoughts becomes your bodily feeling, then the first movement begins." And like Tai Ch'i Push Hands, PetMassage$_{TM}$ movement is action without force. It is fluid and responsive in nature, moving with grace, redirecting any resistance with gentle yielding. Like all martial arts movements, it is your intention that makes your movements powerful and healing.

Your movements continue up through your body to your palms, where you connect with your dog. Your response to how your dog reacts to your touch travels back down your body to your feet, where your next movement originates. The circular path of this movement of intention and Ch'i moves through your Dan Tien energy center of your lower abdomen. Other terms for this center are Hara, or Solar Plexus.

Mom said good posture is important. She was right...again. Here's why. When you keep your feet solidly on the ground, your back straight and your shoulders back, your breathing has an easier, more open path to follow.

Hold your head up. Remember not to slouch or roach your back leaning over your dog. When you do, it compromises your abdominal muscles and stretches your lower back so you will tire quickly. Your dog will entrain with whatever energy you bring to the table. If your energy flow is reduced, his energy flow will be compromised. By the way, also wipe your chin, keep your elbows off the table and don't talk with your mouth full.

Be aware of your body language such as dominance movements of reaching your arm over the dog's withers, or making eye contact. These movements will be interpreted and your dog will think to himself, "I need to move my focus to the outside of my body, where there might be a threat."

Your dog brings to the table the effects of the sum total of all his life experiences. These are genetic, environmental, dietary, training, exercise, accidents, health, love and security. Observe and honor the dog in front of you; create the connection between the observer and the observed. You are both so fortunate to be sharing this time together.

- Get permission from your dog
- Use a table
- Lift with your legs
- Breathe
- All movements start from the feet
- Hold your head up
- Keep your hands in front of your shoulders
- No slouching or roaching your back
- No crossing hands, legs, ankles or feet
- Be aware of what your body language says

**Exercise 29**
**Half empty, half full**

Get on your hands and knees. Pick up one arm. How is the weight transferred? Pick up one leg. Walk a few steps on three legs. Where in your body do you feel strain?

## Chapter 30
## Your Dog's Body Mechanics

The anatomy of dogs is very similar to that of humans. There are two notable differences, though. Dogs still have their tails and we still have our clavicles, or collar bones. You might also have noticed that dogs walk on all fours while humans use two of their feet for walking, and the other two limbs to be used for other functions.

Dogs' spines are more supple, so they can get to parts of their bodies with their tongues that humans can only reach with hands. The action of the four limbs, tail, head and neck, and flexible spine in concert, allows the dog to move in balance as a unified creature.

Each and every movement that your dog creates is counterbalanced by the rest of his body. The tail responds to balance the head. The right shoulder compensates for the left. One hip supports the movement in the other hip. This is *side-to-side counterbalance*. There is natural *contralateral* balance, too. This is the coordinated movement of opposite corners, i.e., left shoulder and right hip. We call this the *corner-to-corner response*. The movements on the same side, such as right foreleg and right hind leg, are called *ipsilateral*.

If your dog has injured his right foot, for example, he will not put weight on it. His body weight is distributed to his other three limbs. So, when he receives his massage session, all four limbs need to be addressed; the one that's been hurt, to increase energy flow to it, plus the three that have been overworked, since they have been taking on the injured leg's share of the work.

You can see his balance and compensating movements in his *gait*. If he bobs his head when putting weight on one of his forelimbs, he is throwing his weight to compensate

> Your dog needs to have his whole body worked during each session.

for discomfort or strain in his leg or foot. If your dog holds his body stiffly, he may be guarding against pain, or his anticipation of pain. If his spine is curved to the side, the muscles on either side of the spine are out of balance, one side being too tight and the other side being too stretched. If he stands with his back roached (arched) he is pulling his spine away from his stomach, where he senses discomfort.

The rest of his body strains to compensate for the strained angulations of his spine and other joints. So, unlike human massage, where we can provide therapy to specific separate parts of the body, your dog needs to have his entire body addressed during each session. The goal is to reestablish balance. Your

> The goal is to reestablish balance.

dog's attention follows wherever you touch him. When he feels discomfort or anxiety when you are working on a particular area, he will distract himself by stimulating another part of his anatomy, licking, or scratching. The licking distraction gives him a sense of comfort and control and can become addictive. It can evolve into a type of self-mutilation. It is not uncommon for dogs to lick their legs or paws raw.

**The integration shake**
After a PetMassage_TM energy session, dogs often will integrate their bodywork with a partial or full body shake. This is the same shake used après bath or to loosen up muscles and joints when walking or playing. When it is a post massage shake though, you can observe it to assess if he had been able to retune his

entire body. If it starts at the nose and works its way all the way to the tip of the tail, with all four legs being shaken off the ground, the session was complete. If the shake only goes as far as the neck, or the mid-back or doesn't include one of the legs, you can see that there is a blockage at the point where the shake stopped. More opening work is needed at the point of blockage.

*Lifting the empty leg*

Dogs need to be supported in their breathing. Their lessons are internalized and often subconscious. They, too, are prone to holding their breath when experiencing pain or learning new skills. To support their breathwork, incorporate into each session respiration enhancement techniques.

Your dog needs to maintain his sense of balance. When standing, he may lean into you, using your body for support. If he's a big dog, this could knock you over. Gently ease him back onto his own feet so he can learn to rely on his own body for comfort and safety. When he is standing, his weight may shift over to one side or the other. Just as when we stand relaxed, we'll often put our weight more on one side. If he is putting his weight on a leg that you would like to pick up, regard that leg his *full* leg and his opposite leg the *empty* one. Shift his weight by pushing him over onto the other leg, making it full, leaving the one you need to lift, empty. Just as it is easier to lift an empty bucket than a full one, it will be easy to lift his empty leg.

## Exercise 30
## Moving the center

Often when you are attempting to pick up a leg, your dog will put his weight onto the limb that you would like to pick up. To make this leg empty and the opposite the full leg, gently push his body toward the side you would like to be full. When he transfers his weight, you can pick up the empty leg.

There is no need to struggle. The session flows smoothly and easily.

Chapter 31
Rhythm and Flow

Each session is a dance. Who leads? The dog, of course.

Each movement of your body starts from the feet and moves up the legs, hips, torso, shoulders, arms, wrists and ends in your hands. Move your feet, hips and torso as you dance your massage session. Feel the rhythm of your movements. Your movements are a dance.

Keep your dog positioned squarely in front of you. If he moves or you need to reach to his other side, maintain contact with one of your hands, walk around to where you can work comfortably. To access the further reaches of your dog's body, instead of stretching with your arms, move your feet.

During the entire massage session, keep your hands in front of your shoulders, with your elbows usually brushing your body in a semi-locked but relaxed position.

When rocking the dog, shift your

A dance.

body weight from one leg to the other, side to side. As your body sways, move his body from your full leg and hand side to the other side as it becomes full. The rocking movement you generate in your spine helps you to effect the movement in your dog's spine. Allow your hips to shift and your whole upper body to sway back and forth. The movement comes from your feet and legs--not from the chest or arms. It really is a dance.

Reactive massage.

Working from the upper torso causes fatigue and your Ch'i will be diminished. Your dog will feel the difference.

One key to maintaining a sense of flow in your work is to maintain your little Buddha smile on your face. It will lift your spirits, lift your head up, correct your posture, remove wrinkles, and put you on the road to enlightenment. It worked for Buddha, didn't it?

## Flow

PetMassage$_{TM}$ is reactive massage. Each reaction to your touch directs you to the next movement. Each section of the massage leads to the next. As your hand is pulled into the dog's field or body, move with it, supporting whatever energetic flow that you sense. Observe your hands as they are held in place and then released. The direction that they are pushed determines where they go next. Allow your dog to control the session. Remember whose massage it is and who is leading the dance.

Keep at least one of your hands touching your dog at all times. You can always alternate your hands. This way, one hand will be the working hand and the other, the supportive hand. This maintains continuity throughout the session. Your dog will feel secure in the knowledge that he is not being abandoned while on the table. As long as he feels your presence he will not experience any disruptive changes in your connection.

*Smoothing* puts closure on each massage segment. A smoothing stroke is an effleurage stroke made either on the body or off-the-body on the edge of an energy plane. It "sets" energy exchange within the limb or area just completed. Once you've finished that part and "set" it, you can move on the next area that calls to you.

### Exercise 31
### Rocking the dog

This is a gentle transference of your dog's weight, attention and intention from one side to the other and back again. When your dog is side-lying, push the body and allow it to naturally return, falling back to center. At the end of the return, gently pull it toward you and allow it to rock back. Continue the motion, repeating it until you sense a freely moving rocking rhythm. Your dog will look up at you when he's complete.

While your dog is standing, stand behind him to rock the rear hips transferring his weight from one leg to the other. Stand next to him to the rock the ribcage back and forth. Stand in front of him to rock the shoulders and neck from side to side. Again, your dog will look at you or move away when he is complete.

This does a number of things. It increases flexibility along the spine, the hips, shoulders, leg joints and cervical joints. It stimulates the intercostals, muscles of the shoulders, hips and legs. As an added bonus, it enhances the bone density of the legs as a weight bearing exercise.

Remember that each of *his* movements start at *your* feet, legs and hips. When you rock your dog, observe *your* body to make sure that it's a-rockin', too.

## Chapter 32
## Energy Mechanics - Your Body

Energy mechanics is about becoming aware of your personal energy fields, enhancing the flow of your energy, grounding yourself, and protecting yourself from negativity. That's a lot!

It is also about sensing your dog's energy field, supporting its flow of energy and draining off its negativity. You are supporting your dog in his/her therapeutic work on physical issues and their supporting substrate of emotional issues.

Energy is high at the ends of meridians, many of which are located on the tips of the fingers and the tips of the toes. Massaging with your fingers, (or your toes), you exchange your Ch'i with that of your dog. Energy is high in the meridian that is most active at a particular time of the day. See Chapter 20, Circadian Rhythms.

**Ch'i has to flow**
The movement of your Ch'i flows with your breath and your blood. When you hold your breath, your Ch'i is diminished. Remember to keep breathing especially while you are learning new skills and while practicing them with dogs. Make a habit of breathing and comfort.

> Allow your Ch'i to flow. It follows open pathways and reduces restrictions.

The center of your body, your Dan Tien, or Hara, is located about 2 inches above and about 2 inches behind your umbilicus. It is midway between your belly button and the anterior (front) of your spine. It is constantly being massaged by the gentle movements of the diaphragm, your primary breathing muscle that stretches across the underside of your thoracic cavity. When you hold your breath, your diaphragm stops its massage and your entire bodily Ch'i is affected. When your breathing stops, the natural flow of energy in your gut stops; and your hands tighten. Your energy field is personal and dynamic. The quality of every breath affects your life condition. Each of your thoughts affects your ability to connect with your dog.

Standing with your weight on one foot, creates a lack of balance, centeredness and grounding. Stay aware of your weight distribution. Stay aware of your connection to the earth.

*No entry sign*

Other common ways you restrict Ch'i are crossing your ankles, wrists, legs or arms.

Ch'i moves along with the blood flow and is amplified by the quality of your connection with source, the earth. Crossing your legs cuts off the blood flow through the groin, the back of the calf and the supporting knee. When you cross your arms, tightness in your chest muscles affects your ability to breathe. This extra strain reduces your energy flow.

*Closed body language* When you cross your feet at the ankles, you are cutting off the grounding energy. Crossing your ankles and sitting "correctly" with only the outside edges of one of your shoes making the connection to the ground is a very weak energetic connection. You are also putting unnecessary pressure on important acupressure points around your ankles.

We know that crossing your arms in front of you puts up a visual and energetic block in body language. Crossing your legs, knee over knee or ankle on knee (the guy way) has the same effect. It has the same look as the "don't do it" sign.

The motion of crossing ourselves is deeply rooted in our culture. I remember as a child if I crossed my fingers, I could tell a fib and it was okay and wouldn't count, (toward what, never occurred to me). Thinking about it now, in energetic terms, the energy of Truth was being cut off.

The crisscrossing motion has an affect on the energetic body. In martial arts, the energetic body can be made vulnerable to attack by "unzipping" it with the motion of quickly swiping the edge of your hand down through the aura from the head to the navel. This was also something we used to do in fencing class in college, to create an opening for a touché. It can be resealed either by zipping it back up or a side-to-side motion with your hand.

As a religious rite, the gesture of crossing oneself with the vertical movement opens and makes your body vulnerable to accept Spirit. The side-to-side gesture seals the deal.

If you are having difficulty connecting with a dog, use this concept and technique. Unzip his energetic armoring by quickly slicing your hands through his energy field,

*This little dog has thick armoring*

moving your hand from his head to his tail. This opens his armoring to allow you in.

He will sense your intrusion into his personal space, so your strokes, once you are inside, will need to be especially gentle and supportive.

Remember to rezipper him when your session is complete. Otherwise it may leave him feeling vulnerable. We all know that awkward feeling of embarrassment when we discover our zipper is down!

> First do no harm.

**Enhancing the flow of your energy.**
Energy is enhanced when you are working with dignity, purpose, love, integrity and the knowledge that you are here to serve.

Grounding.  Before each session ground yourself by taking a couple of deep, even breaths. It reestablishes your connection to the Source. The source is the air we breathe and the ground we walk on. It is life.

The more connected to the ground (grounded) we are, the more comfortable and secure your dog will be. His empathy will be stronger when he is entraining with a sensation that comes to him naturally.  Dogs are by nature more grounded than we are.

Sometimes you may be unsure about how much pressure to use when pressing on your

> Push with your heart, not with your hands

dog's body. PetMassage$_{TM}$ Energy Work maintains the same caution written into the medical oath of practice, "First do no harm." It is always safe to err on the side of gentleness. When in doubt, remember Anastasia's counseling, "Push with your heart, not with your hands."

Also implicit in PetMassage_TM Energy Work is to always have your dog's permission to work with him. All of his movements are his. All of his manipulations are his. All of his adjustments are his. Each of his healings is a choice that he made in his unconscious.

**Exercise 32**
**Push with your heart**

Place your hands on your dog's body. Visualize a force emanating from your hand that presses into his body. Observe his response to this type of pushing. Without moving your hands, project your intention deep inside to his anterior spine. Experiment with pulling, using the same technique. Observe your feelings as you draw your dog's body into your hands.

## Chapter 33
## Energy Mechanics – Your Dog's Body

Your dog's energetic body is similar to yours. The workings are the same. He needs to feel grounded. He needs to feel secure and protected. He can focus on different parts of his body. He can bliss out and experience a meditative state. He can go to sleep. He is easily confused and distracted. He's just like us!

Since dogs' verbal language is undeveloped, they are more responsive to their intuition than we are. They don't have to find the right words to explain complex concepts. Their senses cue them to their relationship to their environment. They flow with it and in it, giving as much significance to a clump of fragrant grass as they do to a human.

In addition to our five senses of feeling, sight, sound, smell and taste, they are aware of barometric pressure, magnetism, ultraviolet influences, pheromones and more.

They have and use more senses than we have ever thought of! See Chapter 26.

One of them is their awareness of their *proprioception,* their situation in space. When he gets on the table, your dog will let you know which direction is more comfortable for him to face.

Allow him to face the way he wants; in his desired direction. Most often, it is toward the areas of lesser distraction and toward harmony.

Dogs intuitively practice Feng Shui in their daily lives.

You have probably noticed your dog following the sun-

light around the room as the day progresses. Dogs seek out the lighting that most enhances their lives. They work on the same natural circadian clock that we

*Oskar follows the afternoon sunlight.*

do. They strive for balance. Dogs require less light at night than during the day, cooler color tones during the summer, and warmer tones during the winter.

See Chapter 44. Full spectrum indoor lamps offer lighting frequencies to support all your dog's chakras.

Turning around three times enables your dog to clear the energetic space before sitting or squatting. Yes, it is also related to your dog's ancient cultural memory of having to flatten grasses or mounds of dirt to create a nest for warmth and protection; he makes energetic nests, too.

Dogs have the natural ability to reestablish balance in their bodies. We see this in their long body stretch when getting up from a nap. The neck and legs are stretched one at a time. The back is arched and the internal organs seem to reorient themselves within the body. One of the best exercises for your dog is for him to chew on a meaty raw bone. His whole body gets a workout as he arches his back and stretches his neck, twisting and ripping with his jaws, all while gripping and bracing with his hindquarters. Even his facial muscles are engaged as his temples contract and his eyeballs roll back into their sockets in bliss!

Your PetMassage<sub>TM</sub> Energy Work facilitates your dog in his quest for balance. Sometimes your dog cannot find all the balance he needs by himself. That's when a jumpstart helps. You're here to help your dog to balance his body in ways he cannot do by himself.

He responds to all forms of massage: on-the-body massage, specific acupressure stimulation, meridian work, chakra balancing and on- and off-the-body healing touch.

*Ting points are on nail beds in hollows behind rear stopper pad and in his dewclaw, scar or. webbing*

**High-energy points**
The tips of his toes and the bottoms of his feet are high-energy sites. Many of the transition points from yin to yang and yang to yin are located on the tops, sides and bottoms of the toes and pads. These points are called *Ting points* and are stimulated to balance the flow of Ch'i through meridians.

The transition acupoints on the ends of meridian lines are some of the most powerful points to stimulate and rebalance his body.

The bottom of his feet, between the pads is also where dogs perspire; where body heat, moisture and scented oils are released. Stimulating the feet and toes helps your dog balance yang heat and increase his flow of Ch'i.

One Ting point that you need to remember is the Bubbling Spring, Kidney 1, located behind the stopper pads under the rear paws. It is a Vitality, or Life Force point that is used for shock, acute seizure episodes and sedation [Snow and Zidonis].

The philtrum, the divot under your dog's nose, GV 27, and the divot under his anus on the perineum, CV-1, are *vitality* points. They are the transition points between the two primary yin and yang meridians, the Governing Vessel and the Conception Vessel. These are especially significant points as they oversee and balance of the entire body. Stimulate them to wake and revive your dog. They are used to revive his life

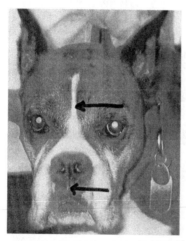

force. Allen Schoen, DVM, in his book, *Love, Miracles and Animal Healing*, calls GV-27 the Cardiac point. He promotes its use to revive dogs and lectures about its value to his veterinary colleagues.

The crease between the eyes, GV-26, called the Third Eye, is sometimes translated from the Chinese as the Upper Dan Tien.

*Philtrum, GV-27 and 3$^{rd}$ Eye*

Stimulating it with light pressure helps your dog relax. Combining this with holding the philtrum, GV-27, helps your dog enter a meditative state.

Holding your dog at the girdle, just above the third lumbar vertebrae, helps him reduce low back pain and increases balance throughout his entire body. Place your thumbs on either side of the spine with your fingers curled into the fold of the flank. Hold this position with light to medium pressure. As a variation, vibrate your hands as you compress or knead with your thumbs over the area.

Other high-energy points are all the transitions of the parts of the skeleton. These are, coincidentally, the major chakra points. Each of these transition points, or planes, needs to be

*Holding dog's girdle*

balanced and coordinated with the other points or planes.

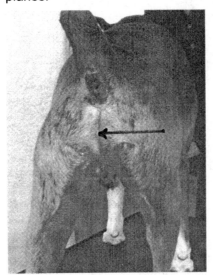

The ridges felt through the upper lip between the teeth are all acupressure points of the Stomach Meridian. Stimulating these points helps digestion, and the entire process to elimination. It effects fear and confidence issues, as well. [Snow].The planes, the locations of chakras and their

*Divot under anus*

referred energy shells must be acknowledged, honored and incorporated into your session.

### Exercise 33
### Ting points

Gently compress, hold and release points on the sides of the nail beds, between and around the pads, the webbing or scar of the dewclaws. Feel for textures. Feel for acceptance or resistance to your touch.

In our human culture, we've learned to stimulate Ting points on infants' toes by playing the "This little piggy went to market," game. There are many really important survival concepts buried in our culture.

Consider all the dogs who are fearful of having their paws touched or nails clipped. This exercise is effective in reprogramming dogs to accept touch on their paws. It is non-threatening and enjoyable.

## Chapter 34
## Release of Energy and Grounding

Negative energy, in the form of sign and symptoms can transfer from one energetic body to another. In other words, unless you protect yourself, you may take on your dog's issues, or he may take on yours. You could walk away from the massage session with sore hips, itchy skin, a runny nose, ringing in your ears or a tight and stiff back. How embarrassed would you feel if you started drooling uncontrollably when you see someone eating an apple or felt compelled to mark your territory when you caught the odor of another person? We won't talk about the overly submissive behavior of flipping over on your back and urinating when in the presence of a dominant dog. No, we won't go there! You also don't want your dog to take on your negative stuff, as if you had any.

*Protect yourself* and your dog by sloughing off the negative energy. Wash your hands before and after each session. Water flowing over hands cleanses your energetic body. This is why showering or standing under a waterfall is so invigorating. If your dog needs to have his energy field cleared, you can pour water over him or hose him down with water. The flow of water through a hose cleanses negativity from the energy field. A simple technique is having your dogs walk through shallow basins or on pads soaked in water and a 1% bleach solution. It cleanses and disinfects their feet; the chlorine helps heal any tiny cuts and (the water) clears their energy.

If you don't have access to water, or don't want the mess, there are other ways to clear his field. You can smudge him and your session room with a smudge stick. This is a bundle of dried herbs that, when lit, produces pungent smoke to cleanse the air of negativity. This is in the tradition of American Indian practices. In the East, the use of incense has been used for millennia.

If you don't want the aroma, here's another way: burn a little Epson salts in grain or rubbing alcohol. We use a pinch of Epsom salts to a quarter-cup of alcohol. The differences before and after clearing the area are palpable. Your room where you will be working will have a fresh feeling of openness and clarity. You can also use unscented white wax candles that burn with purity and simplicity. They too will clear the air.

In addition to, or instead of these spiritual ways of clearing the energy, you may want to consider using an ionizer. It is also effective in helping to cleanse the room of odors. It changes the electric charge of airborne dust particles, causing them to become heavier. They then drop to the floor where they can be vacuumed away.In addition to any or all of the above, make sure you remember to ground yourself and your dog. Negativity, like electricity, will not harm you if you are grounded.

**Visualization for protection**
When you feel vulnerable or overly empathetic to surrounding negativity, visualize yourself surrounded and encapsulated in a white or gold light. This creates energetic armoring; protection from negativity wherever you go. You can project the visualization onto your dog to protect him from the negativity, anxiety and stress of dog shows, agility trials, before large family events, visits to his groomer or vet, etc.

To clear any negativity you might have attracted during a massage, wash your hands with water. No water nearby? Clear your energy field by stroking down each arm with your opposite hand, from your shoulder to your fingertips, proximal to distal with quick medium pressure Effleurage strokes (Smoothing strokes).

Often at dog shows, you won't have ready access to water, so, in these situations, touch the tips of your thumbs and the tips of your middle fingers together, making little circles with your fingers, angle your hands down and visualize the negativity flowing out and away through your outstretched fingers.

It is also useful to pour a little water from a nearby bottle over your hands. Dry them with a towel. You not only wipe away the energetic stuff you picked up while making contact with your last dog, you are also wiping away hair, dirt, sprays, powders and dust. Your next client will appreciate the cleanliness of your subtle and physical hands.

Negativity builds up when you hold your breath. It flows out with your exhalation.

The release of tension in your dog's muscles, fascia, auras and/or mind (spirit) will be seen as twitches, yawns, stretches or the passing of gas.

Changes might not be apparent right away. The releases are not always spontaneous. It may take as long as 48 hours for him to integrate his session. There may be no visible change at all. People are not always aware of the effects of their massages. Why should dogs be any different?

Energy work affects the *entire* body. Many of us who have been trained in Reiki, Healing Touch and other energy forms, have learned to flick away the energy when we have completed a pass with our hands through the auras.

When you think about them, you realize that the fields of energy flowing about your dog's body are open, fluid and vulnerable. Your energy "flicks" that discharge one shell's negativity can have the effect of disturbing the flow of energy within other parts of his aura.

Simplify and quiet your movements by changing your habitual flick to a "drain." See Chapter 35.

Again, touch your thumbs and middle fingers together, angle your hands out and away and release. The drain is spontaneous, elegant and nonintrusive.

*Flick creates disturbance in aura*

Chi' Gung exercises help to ground and center before each session. This one is a virtual energy shower. Stand with your knees relaxed, feet firmly planted on the ground, about shoulder width apart, toes pointed straight ahead. Maintain an even flow of your breathing. The first part of this movement, in the upward direction will be with your inhalation. The second part, in the downward direction will be with your exhalation. (See Exercise 5)

With one slow continuous inhalation, counting from one to ten, move your hands slowly and evenly up from your knees to high over your head, following the contour of your body. As you start your exhalation, slowly and evenly lower your arms, counting back from ten to one, your hands again, following the contours of your head,

> The consistency of the aura reflects your dog's present life condition.

neck shoulders, trunk, hips and knees. Your breath will be just about out by the time your fingers are pointing down. When you get to the bottom, reach down and gather the energy from around the front, sides and back of your lower legs. Bring the energy slowly up over your body with your inhalation and hold it above your head. Take in more air as your hands pause above you. With your exhalation, bring your hands slowly down, counting back to one, bathing your body in the clean, pure energy from above. As your feet sink into the earth, feel your tension drain off.

Move to the rhythm of counting slowly from one to ten on the way up and one to ten on the way down.

I use this Ch'i Gung exercise to ground myself before each PetMassage.
By the 2nd breath cycle, my distractions are gone. I am centered and ready for my next client.

Use this exercise to help you start from a grounded and centered place in your body, your heart and your mind.

Releasing distractions, you open yourself to be guided by your dog to support his/her needs. --JR

### Exercise 34
### Grounding and breathing

Observe your breath as you center your body. Feel your connection to the earth beneath your feet. Feel your connection to the Spirit power above your head. Allow your body to be the conduit for the movement of energy from Earth to Spirit, Spirit to Earth. Allow your breath to adjust to the rhythm of the cycles of energetic flow through your body.

Place your hands on your dog and sense his connectedness to your energy flow.

Place your hands on your dog and sense *your* connectedness to *his* energy flow.

# Unit 9
# Healing Touch

Chapter 35
Healing Touch - Ruffling and Smoothing

Healing touch is just what the phrase implies. With the touch of your hand or the touch of your spirit, healing transformations occur. We've seen how your energetic connection affects awareness and that in turn, effects sensation within the body.

When you are working off-the-body, scan your dog's energetic body with your hands. Sense the variations in the subtle layers of the aura. This is called the *subtle body*. Feel the waves, divots, and variations in pressure, texture and temperature. Heat, cold, fullness, emptiness, heaviness, lightness, sponginess, sadness and/or joy are in the space around your dog's body. When you encounter the edges of layers in the energy field (see Exercise 23), you will feel a tingling or the sensation of weight in your hand. It will have the feel of holding a soap bubble only without the moisture. There is heaviness, but there is no weight. There's shape and bulk, but there is no mass. Energy flows in, around and through other energy. Whatever energy that you connect with is the one that rises up to connect with you.

When you sense resistance within the subtle body, you will want to relax the field. Create a little rake with your fingers by flattening your hand and curling your fingers. This is your little hand-gardening tool to de-tangle the snags in subtle energy. Pull your fingers through using a combing motion. You may feel resistance as your fingers encounter snags of memory or discomfort. Remember to keep breathing. The motion is similar to pulling your fingers through a horse's tangled mane.

The fields reflect imbalances directly under your hands on the body. The areas where you feel the snags are the levels that reflect emotions that contribute to healthfulness. Note the locations where you sense any resistance as your hands pass through your dog's energetic body. Note any sensations of slipperiness or sliding, which would indicate over abundance, an imbalance. You will also feel sadness, grief, joy, loneliness, fear and other emotions as your connection deepens. Detangle, fluff, hold and smooth with effleurage stroking any areas where you feel snags.

### Ruffling
To increase energy flow, use stimulating movements and work in the direction from the rear toward the head and from the body outward. This motion creates excited, yet deliberate fluffing movements with your hands and arms. Think of waving your hands to raise bonfire smoke into the air. Visualize splashing handfuls of water into the air.

### Unruffling
To decrease the flow, to relax and quiet the energy, move your hands in slow, deliberate smoothing movements over the contours of the body in the direction of the lay of the coat, proximal to distal, from the heart to the extremities. Visualize calming the aura with gentle strokes. Work on several different levels over your dog's body. He will guide your hands to his most appropriate level.

> Detangle, fluff, hold and smooth with effleurage stroking any areas where you feel snags.

Where you feel emptiness, or a void of energy, hold both hands over the area, making an oval shape between your outstretched hands. Visualize an energy ball (see Exercise 16) with the stuff of the ball forming a bandage that flows down to envelop your dog's energy wound. You supply the matrix; your dog will fill the gaps with his own healing energy.

246

The energy layers are actually multidimensional planes of the chakras.

> The movements you sense over each chakra
> indicate your dog's current
> physical, emotional and spiritual conditions.

Hold your hands lightly over each chakra. Feel the qualities in the patterns of Ch'i. Feel your hands being pushed or pulled by the wake of energetic flow. Allow your hands to be guided as they slowly move in the energetic wake. You may feel rotating movements. When the movement stops and you feel that that area of the body has arrived at completion and closure, set it with a smoothing stroke and move on to the next area that draws your attention.

Some massage disciplines teach that spiral movements in one direction indicate one type of energy and in the other direction means something else. PetMassage$_{TM}$ movements and their meanings are simplified and elegant. It is not for you to determine what is best for your dog. That is your dog's job!

> Your hands flow in whichever direction
> they are guided by your dog's body…
> giving up control …turning decision making
> to a higher power.

Lift your hands an inch or so further off the body and observe their movements. You are now accessing a different Chakra layer. Allow your hands to move with whatever movements you feel.

**Connecting and balancing the chakras.**
To connect and balance the chakras, hold one hand lightly over one of the chakras and your other hand over another. Connect the odd numbered Chakras to each other, then the even numbered. The odd numbered will all be moving in one direction: the even, in the opposite direction. Hold and follow their movements until you feel that they are coordinated and balanced with each other, moving at a similar rate and strength.

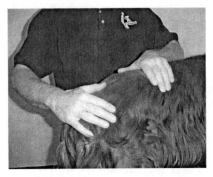

*1 to 3*

Connect chakra #1 to 3, 1 to 5, etc. every other one all the way from one to seven. Then connect #3 to 5 and 3 to 7, and #5-7.

Return to the evens, with 2, connecting 2 to 4, 2 to 6, etc. to 8. Then 4 to 6, 4 to 8, and 6 to 8.

*2 to 4*

Then combine the odd and even numbered chakras by connecting 1 to 2, 1 to 3, 1 to 4, etc. You can spend a lot of time connecting them on several levels; or, you can follow your intuition as to which ones to connect with which. Either way, you are re-establishing balance within your dog's energetic levels.

248

Visualize the color associated with the chakra to reinforce or enhance the effects. If you sense discomfort or anxiety, visualize that the area is coated with a healing light in the colors of green, rose, pale blue, gold or white. Colors have cooling or warming properties. The reds, oranges and yellows are warming. The purples, blues and greens are cooling. Coolness indicates an old wound or chronic situation. When you sense a cool – or cold zone, assist it to a more balanced state by visualizing a warm color in the field. When you sense a hot area, which often indicates recent wounds or acute situations, impress the area with cool, comforting colors. Think of a cool hand on a feverish brow.

Sometimes, the body has a purpose for its heat, such as in the initial healing stages, and its presence is good for the body. In this case, you can assist your dog to a place of further comfort and healing by reinforcing the heat with hot colors, or coolness with cold. You will know, intuitively, how to support your dog to achieve his highest quality of life.

When your session is ending, complete your energy work with Effleurage strokes on the Etheric Double, and/or directly on the surface of the body. This Smoothing-Integration stroke motivates your dog to accept and own his refreshed flow of energy.

Balancing and smoothing helps your dog to attain more balance in his life.

Austin is a Bernese mountain dog who was "volunteered" to be the subject of a final return demonstration at one of our workshops. Austin moved like a slug. His owner, who is also his breeder, said, "He just moves slowly, when he does move. He never exerts himself. I don't think I've ever seen him run." After his massage from the student he was even more relaxed. And since he was already on the massage table, we decided to see what would happen if we ruffled up his energetic body.

I moved my fingers into the heavy field surrounding his body. I pulled and fluffed. I raked and billowed. I was intent on moving and opening up the shells of energy levels. After about 4 or 5 minutes, Austin raised his heavy head, opened his eyes wide and bounded off the table. He ran excitedly around the room several times before he slowed down enough for us to catch him.

His owner stood amazed, with her mouth agape, watching him dash about. She had never in his life, seen him move like that!

## Exercise 35
## Scanning, ruffling and smoothing

Create an energy ball in your hands by frictioning them against each other and cupping the heat. Relax your fingers and wrists. Scan your dog's body by slowly making 3 or more passes over it with your hands. Close your eyes to reduce distractions. Allow your arms and hands to float on the surface of his aura.

Observe your breathing to take you to a deeper, more relaxed state of mind; taking one long, slow breath with each stroke.

Observe yourself as if looking at your body from the corner of the room. See yourself assessing your dog's body. Ruffle and Smooth each area of imbalance that you encounter.

Complete the exercise by rezipping his energetic body

## Chapter 36
## Pain Drain and Energy Boost

Often the physical discomfort that your dog experiences can be sensed in his energetic layers, his subtle body. These will feel like thick snags in the air, or you may feel a heaviness or numbness in your hands, shoulders and neck, legs and feet. These subtle textures may cause you to feel dizzy, nauseous, achy or anxious.

Maintaining contact with your dog's energy using both hands creates a closed physical and energetic circuit. You will be working with your intention flowing through both of your hands. Some of his Ch'i channels up through your hands, arms, across your shoulders and down your other side back to your dog's body. Your Ch'i enhances its movement Maintain your connection using one hand to massage, the other to stabilize or assess his reactions. Your stabilizing hand is sometimes referred to as your "mother" hand."

Anxieties and emotional stressors may develop into diseases if left to their own devises. They would be the root causes. Place one hand on or over the affected area. Have your other hand directed down and out to the side of the body. You are opening the circuit.

*Pain drain moves energy out fingers*

Connection with only one hand channels energy either to or from the other hand. Channeling energy away from the body is called a *pain drain*. It is effective in channeling off discomfort and negativity. It channels stiffness, discomfort and distressing anxieties out of the body.

In this technique, you will only have one hand in contact with your dog's body. Excess energy is channeled away from your contact point through your hand, up your arm, shoulders, down your other arm and out through your outstretched fingers.

When performing the pain drain, make sure you are well grounded so that you do not take on your dog's discomfort, anxieties, etc. This can be a real hazard.

You might be a little embarrassed later in the day to find yourself exhibiting some of his behaviors, like hip soreness, needing to mark trees or pretending you don't hear your name while you are chasing squirrels.

This is the same hand position that you used instead of the energy "flick." Simply touch the tip of your middle finger to the tip of your thumb. Visualize the negative energy, or the pain that your dog is experiencing draining out your extended fingers. The energy transfer is immediate. There is no need for dramatic gestures. It flows out your body at the speed of thought. Touch, it's gone. That fast! That easy! That elegant! That effective!

Use this awareness of his energetic body to help excite your dog's Ch'i. If you sense any stagnation of energy on or around your dog, gently brush your thumb and middle finger against each other, making a silent "snap." According to Traditional Asian Medicine, there are specific places on the body where energy leaks out. These areas are the back of the neck at the skull, the elbows, the hips, the stifles and the hocks. These are also, when you think about it, where the major lymph nodes are located: the Submandibular, Prescapular, Axillary, Inguinal and Popliteal. The snap excites the Ch'i and closes the leaks.

There are some practices that teach if you drain negative energy out, it needs to be replaced with positive energy. Energy is channeled into the body from the outside (the ether matrix). You would use the opposite hand to replace the energy. So, if you were touching your dog with your right hand and channeling the negative influences out your left, when you wanted to replace the energy, you would touch with your left and channel in from your right. In PetMassage$_{TM}$, it is enough to channel the negative out. Your dog has an abundance of Ch'i and what he needs, he will draw to himself, intuitively.

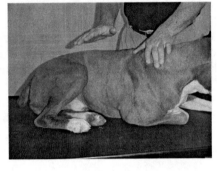

*Channeling Etheric energy in from your right hand*

**Energy Boost**

If, however, you sense that your dog needs an Energy boost in his Ch'i, you can use the reverse of the pain drain to channel the Etheric energy into the area of his body that needs it. Place one hand over the area that feels empty or stagnant. Hold your other hand out to the side above the level of your heart. Direct your intention from the palm of your outstretched hand toward the one on your dog. Visualize and feel the energy flowing from the Ether around you into the raised hand and channeled to your dog-hand. Feel your dog's body fill with abundant healthy life-stuff. This is especially useful working with long-term, chronic, physical or behavioral issues.

## Exercise 36
## Enhancing awareness of dog's energy

Our dogs constantly readjust their own flows of energy to maintain their internal comfort levels. They adjust their energy patterns to enhance our comfort levels, too. The next time you are casually resting one hand on your dog while watching TV, think about how much they are participating; sharing and reacting to your variations in energy.

Chapter 37
Stillness and *Quiet*

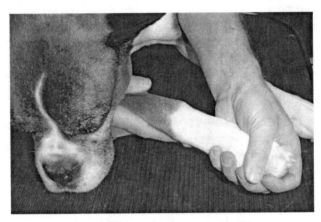

*Holding Oskar's paw in quiet, stillness*

**Stillness**, motionless holding, is an important part of your energy session.

There are times when it is neither necessary nor appropriate to move your hands. Pushing and pulling, kneading and stroking may be distracting from the work your dog would like to be done. There are times when your dog just needs to be held. Pause, and observe the dynamics of your bodies. Pause, and wait for his body to react. Positional release is one example of this. Hold your hands

> Pause, and observe the dynamics of the connections between your bodies.

around or over a point on his body. The waiting time is motionless. The waiting motion is timeless. It is okay. It is therapeutic. Observe the subtle movements under the stillness of your hand. Your patience honors your dog's inner intelligence. It honors your intuitive self.

During the Pain drain and the Energy boost, your hands are motionless. The *exactly right movement* is happening without your interference. The best work happens when, once we have made the connection and placed the dog in the position where they can find their way to a place of comfort, we get out of the way.

This quiet is wonderfully peaceful. PetMassage_TM, in absolute quiet, allows the two of you to move away from all distractions to focus on yourselves and your healing.

Sitting with your dog after the energy session in quiet stillness will have an inspiring effect on your practice and your life.

**Quiet**
The most beautiful benefits of PetMassage_TM happen when there is no music, no dogs barking, the chatter in your mind ceases and you are simply and elegantly present with your dog. Please experience this as this chapter's exercise.

**Exercise 37**
**Experiencing stillness**

(!)

# Unit 10
# Recipe for Success

Chapter 38
Accessing and Balancing Energy Points

Mindful and mindless; each has its place. Each can be a valuable tool.

Refer to the acupressure drawings as you palpate your dog's body. Your attention does not need to be focused on the "healing properties" of the points. In fact, when you keep your mind unfocused, open, and empty, and allow your hands to be guided to where they are needed most, they will be moved or held in place by the magnetism of the acupoints. Then, your primary job is to *observe* how your hands are attracted, drawn in, held and eventually released to move to the next point.

Healing cannot be forced to happen. You are making yourself available to facilitate your dog's physical and emotional transformations. Now, you can let your dog take it from here.

> Healing cannot be forced to happen.

Working the acupressure and chakra points on the dog isn't a separate part of your massage. Incorporate it into each general massage session. After you have completed your assessment routine, and are working over your entire dog, be aware that your hands are accessing meridians and chakras. They are making connections and causing very specific effects. The movements and dynamics that you feel will give you a good idea what your dog is working on, internally. As your hands are pushed and pulled by energy fields recall the meridians and chakras.

If you already know some of the issues that are affecting your dog, use your knowledge of meridians and chakras to assist in his healing.

Balancing energy points assists your dog to establish equilibrium in each point. If you feel your hand pulled or pushed away from any point, this indicates that there is an imbalance in the flow on energy. When your hand is attracted to a point, allow your hand to be pulled in, and held. Re-balance happens when your hand is released. The feeling of the release resembles a gentle sigh from beneath the skin. How long do you hold it? You can maintain contact for 10 seconds, 30 seconds, 5 minutes, or longer. One good indication that your rebalancing is complete is when you either get distracted or unconsciously move your hand away. Subconscious signals from your dog will interrupt your meditation, letting you know when to move on.

When you encounter an area that is especially tender or sensitive, unzip the area and use the Pain drain. Place one hand over the point a couple of inches off the body. The position of your hand is prone, palm down, with the base of your palm over the spot that needs help. Hold your other hand above the dog, supine (palm up) or to the side. If it is prone (palm down), you are keeping whatever is causing the imbalance to stay in. Visualize that the discomfort is being drawn up into your palm and directed to your other hand for release. Simultaneously, positive energy is also attracted and directed into the tender area.

Acknowledge its release. Accept newer, healthier awareness's for your dog with your open hand. Hold that position until your hand is pulled over to the prone position. Your hand will be slowly drawn into the coat to set the new energy design onto the body. Again, the re-balancing is complete when your hand is released.

Working with energy is revitalizing, rejuvenating and life enhancing. Not just for your dog but for you, too. Whatever energy is being channeled into your dog has to go through your body first. If the "wire" of your circuit has some "resistance," and who among us doesn't have a few "issues," your body heats up. It is drawing off some of the Universal Life Force. "Feel the Force, Luke."

**Exercise 38**
**Compression and traction in the field**

As you encounter resistance in a field, use your intention to exert either gentle compression or gentle traction on it. Hold, until you sense that the resistance has dissolved or opened. Continue to observe your breath. Stay grounded.

Chapter 39
Respiratory Enhancement; The Energy Session

Essentially, there are two types of Ch'i: *Prenatal* Ch'i, which is inherited, and *Acquired* Ch'i, which we draw from food and air. Together they form *True Ch'i*. This is the interaction between mind and nature. Breath Ch'i is dependent on the quality and quantity of our oxygen intake and oxygen metabolism, It is essential for the body to function. Breathing regenerates Ch'i.

Part of each session includes enhancing the Ch'i that flows in the oxygen, with the breath, the blood, and the fluids on the body. To enhance oxygen and water metabolism through the lungs and throughout the entire body, you will be focusing on the Bladder, Spleen/Pancreas, Lung, Large Intestine and Heart Meridians. When you focus on the Heart, Throat and Sensory Chakras, you are working the thoracic cavity, the forelimbs and the head.

Sense for energetic armoring around the chest, ribs and diaphragm.

| |
|---|
| Sense for energetic armoring around the thorax: the chest, ribs and diaphragm. |

Assess for tenderness or reactions to your touch. Work the nail beds of each toe, the webbing inside the dewclaw, his philtrum, and the lateral corners of his eyes and nostrils.

**Routine:**
Pre-session, Assess:
 Comfort level of your dog
 Mental attitude (his *and* yours)
 Gait, ease of movement
 Quality of breathing: rate and depth
 Capillary refill, return of pink gum flesh color after pressure

Hydration of body, rate of skin return using pinch test on his chest
Hydration of tongue, color, moistness, presence of mucous, depth of sagittal furrow
Brightness of eyes
Attitude of tail

Session: Start by warming the tissues with frictioning strokes. Using positional release and follow-on movements, stimulate the fascia and muscles in your dog's face, neck, shoulders, pectorals, intercostals, latissimus muscles on his back, and diaphragm. Continue down all four legs including the tops, fronts, sides and bottoms of the paws. Roll the shoulders, roll and rock the body at the head and neck, ribcage and hips.
Create an energy ball between your hands. Use the Clasp Hands technique to invigorate the intercostals, vigorously working from top to bottom and back up to the top, raking through his costal grooves with your fingers.

Firmly percuss his entire thoracic area with cupping. Place one hand over each of the points of his shoulders. Visualize them glowing, and pulsating, filling your dog's chest cavity with the purest of healing energy.

On his body and again, a few inches off his body, slide your hands over the courses of the Bladder, Spleen/Pancreas, Lung, Large Intestine and Heart meridians directly. Balance the Yin and Yang energies with circular strokes over the superior, cephalic aspects of your dog (See Chapter 21). This can be done rapidly and vigorously. Keep your movements fun and joyful.

Assess with your hands or with a pendulum, off the body, over his heart/lung area, his throat and his head. These are his 4th through 8th chakras. Check for the shape and vitality of the movements of your pendulum or the sense of energy movement within and under your hands.

Make sure the directions of the swirls of adjacent chakras are moving in opposite directions.

Use Healing Touch to rebalance and redistribute the energy in and around your dog's body.

To maintain your own flow of Ch'i, ground yourself. Breathe. Maintain correct posture and good body mechanics with your back straight, your knees slightly bent, your head up and your hands in front

> This is fun, isn't it?
> Relax and enjoy the ride.

of your shoulders. Do not cross your feet at the ankles. Do not cross your arms. Keep your hands focused and directed. No "busy fingers," between your purposeful strokes.

**Exercise 39**
**The dance**

PetMassage$_{TM}$ is a dance. Each and every stroke initiates from your feet, where you have your connection to the ground. Push off from the ball of your foot, drawing power from the earth. Follow the surge of energy up through your legs, torso, arms, hands and over to your dog. Follow the return from your dog back down to your feet. When you want to pull your hand away, simply hold your hands where they are and transfer your weight stepping into your back leg. Your body will bring your arm and hand with it when it moves back.

# Chapter 40
## Contraindications

Abdominal massage can cause stomach upset and alterations in blood pressure. For dogs who have concerns about blood pressure maintenance – do not use the clasp hands abdominal lift or massage of the abdominal area immediately after he has eaten his main meal. The blood has been drawn to the stomach for the digestive process and is not available to the rest of the body.

Do not use direct massage on the body, over open wounds or sores, recently fractured bones, or areas of encapsulated cancerous tissue, *or, if your dog refuses to participate in the session.*

For pregnant dams, acupressure is contraindicated in the hock area. It affects hormonal balance and is believed to have the capacity to cause spontaneous abortions. At the time of birthing, however, stimulating this same area, on or around the hocks, can be used to accelerate and support the birthing process.

How often can you provide PetMassage$_{TM}$ Energy Work to your dog? Full sessions are taxing on the emotions and the body. Leave enough time between sessions for your dog to integrate his new information. Up to 3 per week is plenty for anyone. It takes time to reprogram old habits, thoughts and feelings. Not everything happens immediately. Often the effects of massage continue to influence the body for hours, days, weeks, months and years after the session.

> There are no contraindications for off-the-body work.

Energy work, you've already realized, can be useful any time and needn't be restricted to the massage table.

You cannot harm your dog with too much off-the-body work. Your dog will only accept as much as he can handle, so there is no need to be concerned that you are overdoing it.

When the *Effective PetMassage_TM for Dogs* book was written in 1998, it was believed that massage was contraindicated for people and pets with cancer. This view has been reconsidered. So many people found so much comfort and benefit from massage, in spite of the warning that it is now *indicated* by the American Cancer Society as part of most complete treatment programs. The original warning of working deeply over encapsulated areas still holds, though. Effleurage, positional release and energy work are all therapeutic and can be effectively used all over the body.

## Exercise 40
## Observation of dog's integration
## of session, the Integration shake

After your dog has completed his massage, he will usually shake his entire body off the ground. Starting at his nose; he will shake each part of his body in succession all the way to the tip of his tail. This integrates his new post-massage experience into his pre-massage body. His old memories and habits have been reprocessed. He has subtly altered his life-condition.

If he stops his full-body-integration-shake before the end, he is indicating to you that he

1. Feels stagnation or tightness at the point where he stopped.
2. He may also not be fully grounded

Rework the point where his shake stopped or note it for his next session. This is part of his communication process. A complete full-body integration-shake means, "Thank you, for a beautiful session."

Chapter 41
PetMassage<sub>TM</sub> Energy Sequence

This is your basic PetMassage<sub>TM</sub> energy sequence. It is a cookbook style recipe for doing massage. Even if you are increasing blood circulation using Swedish Massage techniques, compressing the muscles, skin and coat, you are still accessing your dog's energy. You are increasing cardiovascular circulation. The Ch'i flows along with the Oxygen in the blood. Consider that the blood is primarily water, which is mostly Oxygen. Ch'i flows in the water in the blood. So, moving the water, moves the Ch'i. Establishing balance in the Ch'i, balances your dog's body, mind, and spirit.

Create an environment that is conducive to massage energy work. Make sure your room is warm to your comfort. Stagnant air is uncomfortable. Be sure that the air is gently circulating. Adjust the lighting so that it is not directly overhead. Use full spectrum lamps whenever possible. Make sure the table height is adjusted so that when you are reaching for the top line of your dog, it is a comfortable reach. If you like working to music, play it at low volume, just loud enough to encourage your mind to "unfocus."

> Allow your dog to relieve himself before the session.

Allow your dog to relieve himself before his session. He should not have just eaten or be ravenously hungry. Give him a final drink of water before putting him on the table.

Center yourself with brief, simple breathing, T'ai Ch'i or Ch'i Gung rituals. When you feel centered and focused, assist your dog onto the table, or if you are working on the floor, settle yourself on an appropriately low stool or pad. Stay aware of your body so that you do not strain your back and arms. Give him a treat once he is ready (optional, but fun) for being compliant...or just for being him.

Allow your dog to move about to face in his/her preferred direction.

Allow your dog to move about to face in his/her preferred direction.

Place your hands on the dog's body, one hand supporting under the throatlatch and the other on the croup. Project your visualization of your dog receiving and accepting this PetMassage$_{TM}$ energy session. Ask him for permission to participate. Get a "yes" response and acknowledge it by either verbally or silently thanking the dog for the privilege of working with him/her.

Balance yourself.

Take your time. Your dog is adjusting his/her body physiology to be sympathetic to your rate and depth of breathing, to your scents, and your intention.

Get Permission.

Assessment strokes are all very slow and deliberate. Their purpose is to connect with the dog on several levels so that both you and he can assess his body.

Start with 3 assessment strokes: Using the heel and palm of your hand, stroke on the body with moderate pressure (the weight of your

Assessment: you enhance your dog's awareness so he can assess his body.

hand) for the first stroke. The second stroke about an inch or two above the body. The third is about 6-10 inches above the body.

Assess and connect to the dog's entire body while he also enhances his own body awareness on all three levels.

1.　Follow the contour of his body over top line, from the tip of his nose to end of his tail (Governing vessel and Bladder Meridians)
2.　Follow the contour of his body down the side of muzzle across his ribs, over his flank, hip and rear leg (Stomach, Gall Bladder, Liver, Kidney and Spleen Meridians). Make sure that you connect with his feet and between the toes.
3.　Follow the contour of his body under his chin across the side of his neck, over his shoulders, down his medial and lateral aspects of his front leg (Triple Heater, Lung, Pericardium, Cardiac, Kidney, Spleen and Large and Small Intestine Meridians). Make sure that you connect with his feet and toes.
4. & 5. Repeat these side passes on the other side of your dog.
6.　Stroke down, starting under the front of his chin, over his throatlatch, his chest and sternum, to his umbilicus (Conception Vessel, Stomach and Liver meridians)

After you've completed the assessment routine, return to the head and start with work on and around his face. Working from behind his head, place your hands on either side of the muzzle, your little fingers supporting his head from under the rami of his jaw. Stroke down the sides of his face with your thumbs, stretching the skin of his muzzle down and away from the gums. Start at the sides of his nostrils (Large Intestine Meridian) and work your way back to his eyes. Compress them and knead them between your fingers. Stimulate his gums around the teeth (Stomach

Meridian) insertions either from within his mouth or from the outside through his muzzle.

Wait for your dog to react to each movement. Hold each touch until you sense that your finger or thumb is released and being pushed off the body.

Gently apply pressure on the sides of his eyes, the Triple Heater Ting points, and the acupoints just above his eyes, Bladder 1 and 2 Acupoints. Wait for your releases, before moving on.

Gently maintain pressure on the Triad, three calming points, one of which is just above his Third Eye and the other two are on the top of his skull, medial to his ears.

Support your dog's head firmly in your hands and fingers as you thumb walk up his sagittal crest. Press and release on the tiny irregularities in the bone along the way and work your fingers around his occipital protuberance at the back of the skull. Smooth across top of skull with the sides of your thumbs to the ears.

Your hands are already cupped around the massiter muscle, the large chewing muscle at the temporal mandibular joint. Press and release moving your fingers in tiny circles, until you sense that his jaw is relaxing.
Move your fingers back into the groove under his jaw, between the rami, the jawbones. Gently stretch them apart and release.
Gently compress the philtrum on the upper lip apart, lightly stimulating the Governing Vessel 27 acupoint.

Use firm pressure across inside and outside of each of his ears, noting any responses to your touch while you follow the soft textures on the outside and the swirls and convolutions inside the ear.

Compress the pinna of his ear, the cartilaginous protrusion and roll it between your thumb and fingers. Fold each ear in half and draw your hand off, slightly shaking and stretching each ear away from its attachment site.

Squeeze the Shock point at the tip of his ear. Hold it until you sense its release or your dog pulls his head away.

Neck and shoulders:

Grasp his coat and skin roll his neck, stretching it from his body. Hold it there. When you feel its recoil from within the tissues begin, allow it to release back onto his body. Continue rolling all around the top and sides of his neck. Place your hands on both sides of his neck and roll it back and forth in your hands. Gently but firmly rock his head and neck from side to side, from one hand to the other.

Support the underside of your dog's chin in one hand and place your thumb and middle finger of your other hand into the indentations under the back of his skull, on either side of his uppermost cervical vertebrae.

Push his chin up so that his skull slides slightly over your fingers.

Follow-on your dog's movements as he turns his head, the back of his skull wrapping around your fingers, to one side.

Hold and release.

Follow his movements as he rolls his head over to the other side, the back of his skull wrapping around your thumb. Hold and release. Repeat this sequence back and forth 2 or 3 times.

Spine:

Skin roll down both sides of his spine to the base of his tail. Each time you grasp the coat, allow your thumbs to access and stimulate the intercostal spaces next to the vertebrae. This is the Bladder Meridian.

Repeat.

Crisscrossing your hands in a rhythmic motion, stroke over his spine with medium to firm pressure. You are compressing, stretching and stimulating his coat, skin, fascia, backstrap, longisimus muscles and supra-spinous ligament, on either side of his spine. This affects his Bladder and Governing Vessel meridians.

Tail:
When you get to the base of the spine, continue down the length of the tail. Squeeze and release the joints between the bones, flexing each segment of the tail to the end and beyond (if the tail has been bobbed). Return to the base of the tail. Grasp it palm down, close to his body, with one hand and stabilize his body with your mother hand on his croup. Gently apply positional release and follow on to his tail, compress-ing it into his sacrum, holding it and observing and supporting his internal movements and releases. Gently guide the tail into its traction position. Follow-on his movements from his stretch to his return.

Stand behind your dog and steadily apply traction on his tail straight out from the spine. Observe him leaning forward and/or rocking from side to side for his optimum stretch.

Smooth with light Effleurage Integration strokes from head to the end of his tail.

Neck and shoulders:
Come back to the sides of his head and ears. Using firm pressure or little circles with your fingers, press and release along the line from the outside edges of his eyes to the base of the ears, following the suture line between his cheekbone and his temple. This is the beginning of the Triple heater Meridian. Continue over and around the top of the bases of his ears, pressing, holding and releasing. Follow the hair texture transition line from his dorsal to his ventral sides, down the sides of his neck to his shoulders.

Stimulate the indentation in the center of the deltoid muscle with light pressure. This is an acupoint to enhance endurance and promote bone strength throughout his body.

The scapula and the upper arm:
Warm the muscles by frictioning and compressing all around the point of the shoulder. With one hand cupping inside his axilla and the other cupping over his deltoid muscle roll his shoulders.

Observe the contours and qualities of his scapula. Follow it up to the top of his withers. Pay attention to the divots, spaces and channels running along its edges where muscles and tendons attach. Compress the scapulas on both sides toward each other, crowding the spine. Hold, release and repeat.

Shoulder and elbow:
Pick up each elbow and gently compress its humerus into the point of his shoulder. This also moves the scapula up to crowd the spine. Observe positional release. Follow-on, guiding his forelegs into gentle stretches to the front. Holding his legs in an extended position, maintain a slight traction to his elbow. Support the structural movements within the articulations in the legs as they respond, readjust and recoil.

Forelegs:
Squeeze and release down the medial aspect of each leg. You can also chuck the muscles, stretching up and gently jerking back down. Pay special attention to the shapes of the contours, the bumps and divots all the way down to the feet. Pay special attention to the hollows in the backs of his elbows. Ease each of his legs down to the ground when is completed. You are supporting the Ch'i through the Lung, Pericardium, Heart and Spleen/Pancreas meridians.

Feet and toes:
Flex and extend the joints in his carpals, metacarpals and toes. Spread the bones of the feet and squeeze and release the webbing between his toes. Touch, hold and release the edges of each of his nail beds. Apply pressure to the bottoms of each of his pads. Spread them, stretching them and squeeze them back together.

Move back up the foreleg to work toward the pectoral muscles in his chest.
Press and release the dewclaw webbing on his medial carpus. If the dewclaws have been removed, gently hold and release the scar from where they used to be. Squeeze and release back up the legs following the contours of the muscles up the lateral aspect of the legs to the axilla. Move to the center of the chest, into the cowlick in front of the sternum. You are supporting the movement of Ch'i in his Triple Heater, Large Intestine, and Small Intestine meridians.

Complete this segment with integrating downward smoothing strokes from his withers to his toes.

Thorax [ribcage]:

Connect the back to the belly by running your fingers down from the top line of the spine, down through grooves of his ribs to the sternum. Clasp your fingers together, release them and rake your fingers back up through the intercostals to the spine – 3 or 4 passes. You are connecting the belly to the back and the back to the belly. This connects the Governing and Conception Vessels, the Yang to the Yin and stimulating the Spleen 21, the Yin-Yang Connecting Point of Connecting Points midway on the 6$^{th}$ rib. At the base of the ribcage, just below the sternum, gently stroke from side to side to the umbilicus. You are stimulating his diaphragm, his Solar Plexus, his Dan Tien, his Hara. You are also stimulating the Bladder, Kidney, Spleen/Pancreas, Gall Bladder, Stomach and Liver meridians and the Conception Vessel.

Hips:
Do the same sequence that you used on the shoulder, on the hips. Before the smoothing stroke, stimulate the three acupoints around the hip joint for 5 to 15 seconds. Then, ground the legs with smoothing strokes. Firmly run your thumbs up the back of the hamstring muscles on the back of the thigh, starting behind the stifle and completing the stroke on the I-T, the ischial tuberocity, or sit bone. This stimulates the Gall Bladder, Bladder, Liver, and Spleen/Pancreas meridians as well as the Governing and Conception Vessels.

Spine:
Moving segment by segment along the spine, starting at the base (tail) press and release the vertebrae making tiny spinal stretches until you feel compression or, compress until you feel expansion. Finish the spine by holding one hand on the withers and the other over the croup. Stretch until you feel compression or, compress until you feel the entire spine. This stimulates the Bladder meridian and the Governing Vessel.

Linear Chakras:
Assess the linear Chakras either with the use of your pendulum or by holding your palms above each energy vortex site. Visualize the color that corresponds to each chakra. Work slowly from the surface of the coat up to 6 to 10 inches off your dog's body. Note any variations in sensations or patterns.

Chakra connecting:
After first assessing and stimulating the Chakras in a line, connect like moving chakras with each other. Connect numbers 1 to 3, 3 to 5, and 5 to 7. Then connect 2 to 4, 4 to 6, and 6 to 8 all the way to the crown. Complete the chakra balancing by connecting the Base (1) to the Crown (8). Visualize the full spectrum of the colors of the rainbow flowing easily and smoothly between your hands.

Auric Chakras/ Energy levels:
Smooth on and then at levels above the body on the edges of his energy shells. Make several long effleurage passes from the head to the tail and beyond. Remember to include the phantom tails of those dogs whose tails have been cropped.

Ruffling:
If you sense any stagnant areas in any of the planes, comb through them with your fingers as if you were detangling the hair in a horse's mane or tail.

Unruffling:
When your hands move smoothly through each of the levels of your dog's auric fields, hold one hand over his withers and the other over his occipital protuberance. Feel the connection and flow of Ch'i between them.

Balance the Yin and Yang energies with circular strokes over the cranial and caudal aspects of your dog.

Assessment:
Finish with one pass of assessment strokes directly on the body. Follow with another assessment pass a few inches off the body. If you sense any stagnation of energy over the back of the skull, the fronts of the hips, the elbows, stifles and hocks, softly snap your fingers over the low energy points to excite and stimulate the movement of Ch'i. When you have completed the pass that moves from the chin, down to the umbilicus, pause and start back toward the front on the midline, connecting the dots.

Connect the dots:
Gently press and release random acupoints along the midline from the umbilicus up the Conception vessel to the chin and then random points on the Governing Vessel from the tip of the tail, GV-Tail, over the top line to the philtrum (GV-26).

Ground:
Ground the dog with deliberate Effleurage strokes from the head and neck down each of his forelegs to his toes and then from the back of his head, along his spine, over his hips and down each of his hind legs to his toes. Make sure that you make complete contact with your dog's paws and toes. Lightly press on the Bubbling Spring, Kidney-1, points on both paws just behind his rear stopper pads.

Connect with the dog for closure:
Place your hands on your dog's body, one hand supporting under the throatlatch and the other on his croup. Observe your breath and your connection with the earth.

Appreciation:
Thank your dog either verbally or silently for receiving and accepting his wonderful PetMassage$_{TM}$ energy session. This can also be a little prayer for his continued happiness.

Calm:
Observe how you feel. Observe your balance. Observe your breathing until you are inhaling and exhaling comfortably and calmly. Stay with him for a short while. Bask in your connectedness and peace.

Completion:
Allow your dog to rest quietly on the table and then assist him/her onto the floor.
Your session is complete.

Review.
At this point your physical session is complete. As he still rests on your table, re-enforce his session, by visualizing a repetition of his massage, or a portion of it. Remember to ask for his permission again, before starting another session.

Clearing negativity on your body:
Cleanse your arms and hands by washing them and
having water flow over them. If no water is available,
use Effleurage strokes from your shoulders to your
fingers to brush off any residual negativity that you
might have taken on from your connection with your
dog.

Clearing negativity in your space:
Clear your space by burning a candle, smudging,
burning the Epson salt-alcohol mixture. You can also
open a window to recirculate fresh air or use an
ionizer.

**Exercise 41**
**Visualizing the PetMassage**

Repeat this massage form by quietly sitting
with your dog and visualizing the massage. It helps to
reinforce the sequence in your mind. It is okay to move
your hands about in space as you retrace your
movements.

Chapter 42
Response at End of Session

After his session your dog may sleep. He may feel relaxed. He may feel energized. He could be confused. He may feel uncomfortable. Your dog may some need time to get used to his altered state of energy flow and balance. It may take 24 hours, an entire circadian cycle for him to integrate his PetMassage. Each session is different. Each dog will have a uniquely different experience with each massage.

> After the first time I experienced acupuncture, I felt disoriented, confused, angry and surly. The feeling lasted for about 2 days. The experience taught me that our bodies and spirits are intricately interconnected.
>
> The slightest imbalance in the yin or yang of any organ system can seriously impact outlook, mood, and self-esteem.
> --JR

As you progress through the session, your dog will most likely move from a standing position to a sit. From there, it is only a matter of time before he slumps onto his tummy and from there onto his side. If he falls into a deep, trance-like state allow him to rest for a few minutes before gently rousing him. Then, he can be awakened and gently unruffled above and directly on his coat. It is a fun place for him; connecting with his true nature.

## Exercise 42
## Post massage observation

Observe the different behaviors that your dogs exhibit after their PetMassage<sub>TM</sub> sessions. Note how long it takes for them to rejoin family activities. Often, they may need to spend some serious "cave time," giving their bodies time to readjust to their new emotional and electrical programming.

# Unit 11
# Exploring New Levels

Chapter 43
Perspiration

**Skin**
Skin is part of the protective pouch that contains your dog's body. It consists of layers of tissue, moisture, oils, pores, hair follicles and lots of sensory corpuscles to detect heat, cold and pressure. These corpuscles are so sensitive that they can feel the presence of a mosquito or a fly when it lands on the coat. Realizing just how aware they are to the slightest pressure helps us understand that PetMassage$_{TM}$ strokes needn't be deep to be effective.

There are significant differences between the ways humans and dogs perspire. Humans perspire through their skin. In the human body, the skin is the largest organ. Through the process of perspiration, humans release moisture, which evaporates and cools the body. In addition to water, sweat contains salt and urea, a natural waste product of body metabolism. So, sweating is a way for us to excrete water, urea and salt from our bodies. If we couldn't sweat, we would have an overly acid internal environment filling up with toxic uric acid. And, we'd overheat and be running to the bathroom all the time.

Dogs can only wick off moisture and the other components of sweat through evaporation from their tongues and the spaces between the pads of their feet. They have another way of cooling themselves. They use the process of conduction, in which heat or cold is transferred to or from the dog's body into whatever he is touching. The ventral aspect (undercarriage) of the dog has thinner skin and finer hair than the dorsal (topside). This is why your dog can find relief from the summer heat by lying on their tummies in a pool of water, on cool concrete or in cool dirt. The dorsal aspect has thicker skin and hair. In the winter dogs will curl their bodies to keep warm, exposing only the outer heavier coat to the harsh elements.

Dogs pant at different rates. We've already seen how strokes can stimulate or relax, depending on their direction. Some PetMassage$_{TM}$ strokes can increase your dog's respiration rate, causing him to pant more vigorously. Or, you can relax an overly anxious dog who may be apprehensive or overheated. Use off-the-body strokes, with the same relationship of direction to function to have similar effects on the layers within the aura.

**Exercise 43**
**Table tracks**

Observe the sweaty paw tracks on your massage table while working with dogs. It is normal to see them diminish as the session progresses.

Chapter 44
Vibrations

Your dogs' bodies, like our bodies, are made up of
trillions of vibrating atoms. At the densest they are the
physical bodies that we can see, smell, hear, taste and
feel. In addition to touch and intension, their core
vibrating elements are affected by light, sound, and
temperature. The vibrations in their extended subtle
bodies are residuals from soul lessons and memories.
They are emotion-based; and like our emotions, can
be affected by the vibrations of external stimuli.

**Color, using color in your practice**
Each color in the visible light spectrum has its own
measurable wavelength and frequency vibration. The
effects of color on dogs are similar to the effects on
humans. The color spectrum is identified with the
individual chakras. Your dog's physical and behavioral
issues can be affected by supplying the appropriate
corresponding color to his visual diet.

| Chakra | Color | Behavior |
|---|---|---|
| Root | Red | Basic instincts |
| Sexual | Orange | Prime directive: Reproduction |
| Solar Plexus | Yellow | Know place in pack, fear: Transition |
| Heart | Green or Rose | Seat of inner knowing, confidence |
| Throat | Blue | Vocalize. Overt barking, cough |
| Sensing | Purple | Viewing outside world |
| 3rd Eye | Indigo | How dogs see themselves |
| Crown | Violet | Connection to Top Dog |

Color therapists use cool tones such as blue, green,
purple and violet to balance hot conditions such as
inflammations. They use warmer tones; red, orange
and yellow to balance cool conditions such as poor

circulation and the scarring over old wounds. They use information such as in the chart above, for emotional issues. Use colored lights, fabrics, collars and visualizations (Chapter 25, Bassett Hound) as tools to enhance your dog's massage.

| | | |
|---|---|---|
| Red | Vitality, courage, self confidence. | Use for timid animal, or if he needs extra energy |
| Orange | Happiness, confidence enthusiasm. | Helps to be more independent, self-assured and social |
| Yellow | Mental ability, versatility, fear. | Promotes playfulness & flexibility in rigid dogs |
| Green | Balance, love calmness. | Brings feelings of peace, harmony and love |
| Blue | Health, knowledge, relaxation. | Calms hyperactive and nervous dogs |
| Indigo | Sedative, calming, intuition. | Telepathic communication, clears anger |
| Violet | Soothing, inspiration, creativity. | Inspires during training & difficult tasks, dispels depression |

If you are unsure about using specific colors or what the issues are that need to be addressed, use full spectrum light. It is the same as the light from the sun. It has rejuvenating and balancing properties.

There are more vibrational influences you can use in your practice to affect the quality of your dogs' lives.

## Nose and Pheromones

### Nose

We all know how good a dog can smell, especially when he comes inside after playing in the rain! Dogs are especially aware of fragrance and vibrating energy molecules in the air around them.

Your dog's nose and the points surrounding it are enormously important in energy work. The exterior of the nose is highly pigmented. Pigmentation, texture and moisture all are behaviors that you can read and analyze. Their normal conditions are the baselines for perceiving any imbalances. The edges of the nostrils are the end points of the Large Intestine Meridian, that continue across the side of the dog's face, down the shoulders, through the dewclaw and down to the second toe. The sides of the nostrils affect and are effective in rebalancing the elimination and absorption part of digestion. The points by the dewclaws are Life Force points, helping to reduce pain and enhancing the immune system. Since the *ting* points affect the entire meridian, the point on the dewclaw is stimulated when you touch the side of the nostril.

Just below the nostrils is the philtrum, the medial gap that separates the two sides of the upper lip. This is another Life Force point. It is the endpoint of the Governing Vessel Meridian (GV-26). Known as the Cardiac Point (Schoen, Miracles and Animal Healing) it is successfully stimulated to revive dogs that have cardiac infarctions or intense shock.

### Pheromones

There is a small sensory unit on the upper palate of the dog's mouth behind the nose, just behind the front teeth. This is the Jacobsen's organ. Recent research has described its significance and function as being able to *taste* smell. Using this organ in concert with his two nostrils your dog can figure out where scents originate, to triangulate. This gives them the ability to track and locate victims buried deep under snow or disaster sites. Dogs are normally nose breathers. You may have noticed that their mouths are slightly open when they are checking out unusual scents such as other dog piles.

Humans have this organ, too. It is in the same position, on the roof of our palates. It is with our Jacobsen's organs that we can "taste" fear, "taste" the sweetness of success, and sense when we are either comfortable or uncomfortable with others. We are interpreting the scents they exude from their body chemistry. The perfume industry has been using these concepts for millennia.

Interestingly, when you practice martial arts or yoga, you learn to lightly touch the roof of your mouth with the tip of your tongue. It is also the point where the Yang Governing Vessel meridian transitions to the Yin Conception Vessel. This connects your yin and yang natures.

**Aromatherapy: Essential Oils**
Aromatherapy can be an effective tool in massage. The tiny molecules of the aroma work not only through the nose, they infuse transdermally and subconsciously, as pheromones. For the aromas to be most effective, they only need to be in very small doses, barely enough to be detectable by smell. Many practitioners feel that "more is more," and can overwhelm the senses with fragrances. Aromatherapy, whether used correctly or not, is effective for people. It has been used successfully for many years to help with physical and emotional issues.

*Essential oils* are a class of volatile oils, extracted from plants, fruits, or flowers, each having its characteristic odor, and hot burning taste. They are available in the form of highly concentrated solutions. They have different effects on human bodies and psyches. Some are relaxing; some, stimulating. Some have medicinal values. Lavender and Tea Tree, for example, are uses as disinfectants. Eucalyptus, Spruce and Peppermint are known to be effective in clearing sinuses and alleviating pressure headaches. Their use needs to be carefully controlled because too much, too concentrated, or the incorrect mixture of oils can be detrimental.

There are many aromatherapy practitioners that maintain that since it works for humans, it must, by extrapolation, work just as well for animals. There is not good evidence that aromatherapy is as effective with dogs. Somewhere in our history, our response to various aromas and chemicals (pheromones) was encoded in our DNA. It was only encoded in human cultural memory.

Dog's have different and distinct cultural memories. They are a different species, with different responses to odors and chemicals. They respond to such exotic smells as garbage, rotting fish and the feces of other dogs. If you were to burn candles or light incense with *these* scents, your dogs would be truly grateful! Remember whose massage session! Remember whose cultural memory!

> Remember whose cultural memory!

Your dog senses smell many times more intensely than we do. Colognes, after-shaves, perfumes and body lotions all contain essential oils. Their purpose is to enhance your smell. In other words, to cover up how you truly smell and who you really are. They cloak your health, your confidence and your intention. There are many dog trainers who believe that if they suck on a peppermint lozenge, their dog will not be able to sense their apprehension. We know better, though. Dogs are too discerning to be fooled that easily.

We've all been around people who use fragrances that battle with their natural body chemistry. The results are cloying and foul smelling. Please do not be one of them. Dogs appreciate honesty and directness. Cleanliness is not very high up on their list of priorities. Your natural scent alone yields enough information to please any dog.

For the relief of all the people and dogs around you, keep your fragrance as neutral as possible; it will have nominal effects on your dog's sensitivities. For his massage to be successful, his awareness needs to be directed inward, with as little distraction as possible toward extraneous odors. He needs to be comfortable and secure with the person who is working with him.

If you are already a proponent of aromatherapy, use a tenth of what you are already using. Think of it, as "less is more." Your dog will have a more powerful reaction and, more importantly, you'll get the effects that will help to make you a better vehicle for his massage.

CAUTION: Essential oils are not to be used directly on skin. They can cause irritation and burning. Use clay rings that fit over light bulbs with a drop or two of essential oil. The aroma will evenly disperse throughout your room as the bulb heats.

**Flower essences**
Flower essences are water-based solutions, which contain the essential energies of flowers. They work on a much more subtle level. Unlike essential oils they are unscented and unflavored. Through special preparation, essences contain only the energetic properties, or vibrations, of the flowers or plants. The preparations are diluted and stored in brandy, distilled water or vinegar solutions.

Flower essences work by resonating with the body's electrical system. This system consists of four levels, the physical, emotional, mental and source. When electrical circuits are broken or overloaded, imbalance and dysfunction occur in the corresponding level. Flower essences reconnect and balance the circuitry so healing can take place.

Muscle testing is used to determine the best essence combination. Flower essences are usually taken orally, but can also be applied topically. They do not interact with food or medications. They are used for health challenges, going through transitions, dealing with mental or emotional issues, growth and healing.

The Bach Flower Rescue Remedy and other homeopathic flower essence remedies are helpful tools when working with animals. The vibrational effects can be calming for several emotion-based issues such as territorial obsession, fear, separation anxiety, lethargy, grief, confusion, and more.

Most of the dog trainers, handlers and vet tech's that I know have a bottle of Rescue Remedy in their kits. It helps calm overly excited or fearful dogs.

Use flower essences as a support to your manual PetMassage$_{TM}$ and energy work. It will help your dog to focus on his healing. Whereas we find that the use of aromatherapy can be distracting and risky, we can understand the benefits of combining flower essences with PetMassage$_{TM}$ Energy massage.

**Exercise 44**
**Smell this**

Break open a ripe green pepper and sniff its aroma. Press your nose deep into it and inhale deeply through your nose. Multiply this effect times ten and you have an idea of how intense aromas are to dogs. Dogs can detect odors over 100 times that of humans.

Chapter 45
Developing Intuition

Trusting your intuition comes with practice, experience and trust. Listen to your heart. Trust what you know to be true.

> Listen to your heart.
>
> Trust what you know to be true.

All of our wisdom and cultural memories are stored in the matrix of the Ether, in the Akashic Record. Dogs' cultural memories are stored there, too. The Ether is the stuff that makes up the space of the universe. This is the space between planets and the spaces between cells. It's the space between thoughts that Dr. Deepak Chopra calls the *gap*. This is the reservoir of wisdom in the spaces between our blocks of self-talk and inner chatter that we tap into during meditation; the cellular memory in our fascia that directs us to positions and places of comfort and healing. It is the reservoir that we access during each touch and with each positional release. This is the river referred to in the introduction. The Ether, or Etheric, is the substrate upon which the energy swirls. We see its wake in the movements of a pendulum around chakra vortices.

The following reflection is one meditation about the earliest example of pet massage.

**Caveman and dog**
We can easily visualize a caveman squatting on a rock in the circle of light around his fire. He crouches, methodically rubbing his shoulder. See him ease his pain.

Dogs have been companions and hunting partners with man since the earliest of times. Bones of dogs have been found along with early human remains and other prehistoric archeological artifacts.

Dogs and humans provided services to each other. In return for scraps of food and shelter, early dogs would bark to alert early humans to danger and may have helped them in their hunting. They were begging at the table even then.

How much of a leap is it to visualize an injured dog, limping into the circle of warmth around the fire; attended by the healing touch of the caveman, or medicine woman? This image is so real that it takes on its own ring of veracity. It is truth. It is part of our cultural memory. PetMassage is an extremely old skill. It is the oldest, most natural, and most instinctive self-health care.

> No one has ever worked on the exact same animals as you or has seen your results.
>
> Your practice is creating history.

Therapeutic massage is *the* most basic fundamental holistic health care. Every human culture since the dawn of time has developed massage techniques for both therapy and pleasure. Throughout the world, until the last 100 years, and then only in western first world countries, it has been the *primary form* of healthcare.

One way to develop confidence in your work is to track your work and experience. Keep a log of what you have done. Ask your clients

> Journal.

for testimonials and permission to use them in your advertising. Save your especially rewarding or noteworthy experiences and press clippings in a scrapbook. Journal.

In two or three years, you will look back to recall the thoughts, feelings, fears and victories you had as you grew. These are reminders of the good work you are doing as you develop your skills; helping dogs find health and happiness.

**Exercise 45**
**Distance PetMassage™ Work**

Visualize a dog that is not in your presence, on the table in front of you. Ask his permission to participate in the session. After you've sensed that you have his acceptance, visualize the all or part of the massage, sequence by sequence. It may help to move your hands to know/sense the contours of his body and the qualities and textures of his energy.

You can work on animals across the room or across the country. Energy exists outside of time and space.

## Chapter 46
## Summary

All of us, including our dogs, have a tendency to hold our breath while learning new skills, or when we are startled or when we are traumatized. Remember when you jammed your toe into a crack in the sidewalk and gasped with pain? The angst of the experience was trapped in your cells by the explosive pressure of your held breath. If you had continued breathing through the pain, the memory of it would not have taken root. We have to keep breathing to maintain an even flow of Ch'i.

When we stop breathing, the Ch'i gets crammed together creating a block of energetic resistance. These blocks are stored as memories in the tissues. When enough blocks build up or if a particular spot of the dog's body gets triggered by a physical or emotional event, the memories in the blockage can surface to create muscle knots, swelling, and even pinched nerves. Blocks are observed as tenderness to your touch. You can see them as lack of coordination in gaits, pacing, unexplained lameness that moves from limb to limb, stiffness, partial weakness or paralysis. They may show as a change in your dog's demeanor.

Each time you connect with your dog, his body's internal intelligence conveys messages from deep within his joints, muscles, fascia, blood and other tissues in his body. As you support one of his limbs in positional release, for example, his body is making unconscious choices. It is making decisions about which way and how much to move to find a more comfortable position. The fact that a decision is being made implies that there is not only awareness in the area, but also memory. Choices are made because of the memories of times when there was more comfort and times when there was discomfort. This is muscle memory, in which a limb or joint is held in a fixed, protected position.

All PetMassage$_{TM}$ Energy Work is therapeutic work with your dogs' permission. Our tools are touch, positional release, acupressure on points on the meridians, on- and off-the-body chakra and auric balancing.

> The intent of this work is to reestablish balance in our dogs' lives.

Stimulating or relaxing your dog, you effect changes on his physical, emotional and spiritual levels. While spiritual may not be an often-acknowledged state for dogs, in their quest for internal wisdom to make sound decisions about their comfort and healing they do tap into the same gap, and the same Akashic Record, as do we.

> The intent of this work is to assist dogs to reestablish balance in their  lives.

There are gaps or spaces between each of the cells, between muscle fibers, within every joint capsule and even between thoughts. Within these gaps is the storehouse of all life's conscious and subconscious thoughts and feelings. It is the dynamic awareness of the universe. From within the gaps comes the awareness that tells the dog which way to move to comfort.

The wisdom of the gap is not limited to your dog's temporal experiences. Your dog may be working through memories from a previous life, or from his cultural memories locked deep within his genetic traits, embedded deep within his muscle memory.

The movements of the Chakra vortices leave a wake in the Ether. This is the substrate of Life Force, the same stuff that makes up the gap. The network of meridian power lines runs via the gap. The fields of energy that flow around your dog are gap. If you were to add up the amount of gap compared to the amount of physical tissue, you'd find that your dog is 99 per cent gap! Your dog is truly a creature of the Universe. He is a creature of God.

Working in the energetic levels, you bypass your intellectual nature and connect with your intuition in your unconscious. From this level you can connect with your dog's intuitive powers, his unconscious nature. This is where change and healing can truly take place. We've seen that our intention and our purpose, along with technique, dramatically affect our dogs' quality of life.

PetMassage assists older and infirm dogs to become happier and healthier. It helps young dogs handle the pain of growth spurts. It helps dogs with emotional issues learn to cope with them. It helps the most well adjusted dog to enjoy his life more fully. Stay within our scope of practice, remember to "Do no harm," remember that this is reactive movement massage. Maintain patience as you wait for your dog's response to each touch to guide you toward your next movement in his massage.

In a recent interview, I was asked, "Which dogs need a massage?" My answer was easy. "All dogs!"

Energy is Power. Power is Energy. PetMassage$_{TM}$ Energy Works with Dogs provides you with the abilities, awareness' and knowledge to support your dog's intuitive healing abilities. Love is Energy. Use the Power of Love in your work.

# Unit 12
# The Future

Chapter 47
This is the Future

More and more, people are searching for and finding more holistic approaches to animal care. They find therapies they can learn to use to complement traditional veterinary care. They have rediscovered Traditional Asian Medicine and acupuncture. They have discovered Reiki, Healing Touch, flower essences, homeopathics and animal communication.

*Touch* is the fundamental way that people connect with their dogs. And the touch of the physical and spiritual connects all of us profoundly together.

With compassion and understanding, developing expertise through your practice, you will learn to enhance the quality of your connection with your dog. In other words, your love will grow.

Can you achieve in this field? Yes. The signs of acceptance are all around us. Advertisers have discovered that the way to customers' hearts is through images of animals. Entire cable television networks are devoted to showing animal stories. Supermarket-style pet stores market everything and anything to pet owners who are eager to find more ways to help (and spoil) their pets.

Human massage has grown in popularity and acceptance in recent years. It is now an accepted part of medical and rehabilitative therapy as well as spa programs. It is just a matter of time before PetMassage$_{TM}$ gains similar acceptance.

The field of PetMassage$_{TM}$ is new. It will take cultivating and marketing skills to educate your clients that what you do is available, accessible and necessary. Most people, whether they've personally experienced massage or not, already believe that massage is helpful and therapeutic.

Demonstrate the credibility of PetMassage$_{TM}$ to veterinarians and other pet owners wherever you go. Once they have an inkling of the potential health and behavioral benefits they will enthusiastically support your growth.

At the time of this writing, there are an estimated 75 million dogs in the United States alone. One in three families own a dog and most of them have 2 or more dogs.

So, demographics are right, the interest is obviously there and pet owners are eager to learn more about and access complementary animal health care.

The potential of PetMassage$_{TM}$ is huge. Look at the signs all around us.

---

Upon entering the little country store, the stranger noticed a sign saying DANGER! BEWARE OF DOG! posted on the glass door. Inside he noticed a harmless old hound dog asleep on the floor beside the cash register.

He asked the store manager, "Is THAT the dog folks are supposed to beware of?"

"Yep, that's him," he replied.

The stranger couldn't help but be amused. "That certainly doesn't look like a dangerous dog to me. Why in the world would you post that sign?"

"Because", the owner replied, "before I posted that sign, people kept tripping over him."

---

The timing is right. Your future is bright.

I congratulate you for taking the initiative to learn these skills and having the foresight and courage to be in the vanguard of the field of PetMassage<sub>TM</sub>.

Thank you for allowing me to share my dreams and insights with you.

Namaste.
*--Jonathan Rudinger*

## Chapter 48 Elizabeth's Poem

After completing one of our workshops this student felt compelled to write this poem. *Elizabeth Hammer, August, 2000*

Open yourself to a world of pure joy.
Hands to paws,
Ears to palms,
Fingers in valleys.
Let you spirit soar
On the gentle creature you are with,
Who gives you loving nuzzles.

Your hands will become like birds who
Learned to fly with a gentle  grace all their own.
You will discover a new part of yourself,
And don't be surprised if a dog
takes hold of your heart,        Bringing a tear and
twinkle to your eye.

You will enter a realm of experience,
which will transcend you and your animal friend,
to a deeper relationship ... one full of gentle soothing
strokes, relaxation and pure pleasure for you & your
furry friend.

For you have been given a gift which you now can give
to others.
A gift from heart to hand – hand to heart.
A furry face gently falls into your hands, ready to
embrace,
Touch that they willingly receive...if gentle, loving and
devoted wholly to them.

My hands have discovered a new world.
Let them be open and ready for the big, the small,
The young, the older, the new, the familiar,
And the bountiful variety of people and their furry
critters who come my way.

This is a journey...one with whom my hands and
heart, will find a place to rest...
gentle and attentive...to what they find.

Push with your heart.

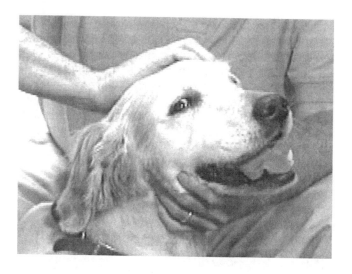

PetMassage is a harmonious connection
with your pet.


Return to innocence.



Unless you are working with the
lead-dog,
the view never changes.

## Suggested Reading

Your study of PetMassage$_{TM}$ Energy Work has just begun. You will continue to learn with more experience.

Our greatest teachers are our canine clients. Listen to them and heed their instructions. Listen to your heart and you will always be right. Attend as many workshops by as many people as you can. There are as many styles of animal massage, as there are therapists. Even redundancy of the techniques and theories you may have learned in previous classes will be heard and understood in a different way when taught in a new context, by a different person, to a new you.

This is a list of some of the sources that were used as references for this book. I suggest you find them, study them, and refer to them often, as your experience and understanding grows. These books and tapes contain thousands of "Aha's."

Ball, Stefan, Judy Howard, Bach Flower Remedies For Animals, Saffron Waldon, The C W Daniel Company Limited, 1999 [Flower essences, homeopathics]

Beck, Mark F., Theory and Practice of Therapeutic Massage, Milady Publishers Inc., 1994 [Medical – Human massage]

Brennan, Barbara Ann, Hands of Light, A Guide to Healing Through the Human Energy Field, Bantam New Age Books, 1987 [Metaphysical – Healing Touch]

Caras, Roger, A., A Dog is Listening, Summit Books, 1992 [Naturalist]

Fox, Michael W., The Healing Touch, Newmarket Press, 1981 [Veterinarian]

Goodman, Saul, The Book of Shiatsu, The Healing Art of Finger Pressure, Avery Publishing Group, 1990 [Shiatsu]

Hourdebaigt, Jean-Pierre, RMT, Canine Massage, A Practical Guide, Howell Book House, 1999

Huang, Al, Embrace Tiger, Return to Mountain, Moab, Utah: Real People Press, 1973.

Jou, Tsung Hwa, The Tao of Tai-Chi Chuan, Way to Rejuvenation, Tai Chi Foundation, Warwick, New York, 1991.

Rudinger, Jonathan C., Effective Pet Massage for Dogs, Volume One video, PetMassage, 1997 [Instruction], Effective Pet Massage for Dogs Manual, PetMassage, 1998 [Instruction] Effective Pet Massage for Older Dogs, Volume Two video, PetMassage, 1998, et al [Instruction]

Rugaas, Turid, On Talking Terms with Dogs: Calming Signals, Legacy By Mail, 1996 [Communication]

Schoen, Allen M., DVM, Love, Miracles, and Animal Healing, Simon & Schuster, 1995 [Acupuncture]

Schwartz, Cheryl, Four Paws Five Directions, A Guide to Chinese Medicine for Cats and Dogs, Celestial Arts, 1996 [Veterinarian – TCM / Acupuncture]

Snow, Amy & Zidonis, Nancy, The Well-Connected Dog, A Guide to Canine Acupressure, Tallgrass Publishing Co., 1999 [Acupressure]

Yang, Dr. Jwing-Ming, Chinese Qigong Massage, General Massage, YMAA Publication Center, 1994 [Qigong]

## Appendix 1 Terms

### Directions and descriptions
Dorsal. Upper side or top of dog's body
Ventral. Under side or bottom of dog's body
Cranial. Front, referring to head
Caudal. Rear or bottom, ref to tail

Superior. Above
Supra- (abbreviation) above
Inferior. Below
Sub- (abbreviation) under

Proximal. Closer to midline of body
Distal. Further away from midline of body

Midline. Center of body i.e. spine is midline
Sagittal plane. Vertical plane through longitudinal axis of
    the trunk dividing the body in two portions

Lateral. On the outside of the limb
Medial. Toward the middle, on the inside of the limb
Contra lateral. Originating in or affecting the opposite
    side of the body
Ipsilateral. On or affecting the same side

Prone. Facing downward.
Supine. Facing upward.

Inguinal. In the groin
Lingual. Refers to tongue

Crest. Ridge or elongated prominence
Protuberance. Bulge, a part that is prominent above the
    surface, like a knob

Valley. Indentations on skin, between muscles, at joints
    between vertebrae, ligaments, tendons, between
    ribs, over sinuses and suture lines of skull.
    Acupressure points locations

## Movements

Abduction. Movement away from midline of body
Adduction. Movement toward midline of body

Pronation. Turn belly down
Supination. Turn belly up

Protraction. Extension. Moving body part back away
    from midline of body
Retraction. Pulling body part back toward midline of
    body

Flexion. Movement toward midline of body
Extension. Movement away from midline of body

# Glossary

**A**

Acupoints. Acupressure points

Acupressure. Use of fingertip pressure on point on surface of the body to regulate flow of Ch'i

Acupuncture. Use of insertion of needles to regulate and balance flow of Ch'i through specific points on surface of body

Adhesions. Muscle fascia stuck on muscle fascia

Akashic Record. A theosophical term referring to a universal filing system which records every occurring thought, word, and action. The records are impressed on a subtle substance called Akasha (or Soniferous Ether). The records have been referred to by different names including the Cosmic Mind, the Universal Mind, the collective unconscious, or the collective subconscious. Akashic records make clairvoyance and psychic perception possible

Anatomy. Study of body parts. What it is

Articulation. Joint

ADP. Adenosine diphosphate is produced during muscle contraction. It is reformed during the muscle relaxation phase

ATP. Adenosine triphosphate, present in all cells, but particularly in muscle cells, produces phosphates and energy when acted upon and split by an enzyme (adenosine triphosphatase). Carbohydrates, proteins and fats are utilized in the production of ATP

Aura. Spiritual or emotional body surrounding and flowing through physical body

Axilla. Armpit, area of chest under front arms

**B**

Backstrap. Band of fascia-ligament that runs over the spine, skull to sacrum

Balance. Symmetry of energy flow, equilibrium

Bursa. Fluid filled sacs: cushions between the skin and
tendons, and tendons and bones that aid in
movement as tendons glide over bones and
other tendons

## C

Carpus. Wrist

Caudal. Rear or bottom, referring to the tail

Cephalic. Head, Front

Chakras. Energy centers located on etheric double
layer
8 Major Points: Root, Sexual, Solar Plexus,
Heart, Throat, Sensing, 3$^{rd}$ Eye, Crown

Chucking. Techniques used to stretch and release
tissue on the limbs

Connective tissue. Tissue that supports other tissues
and parts. Highly vascular (except cartilage)
few cells, mostly matrix

Cranial. Head, referring to the part of the body close to
the head

Croup. Point over the hips

Cupping. Type of percussion/tapotement in which your
rounded hands (cupped) are slapped onto the
body giving a hollow sound

## D

Dewclaw. Non-essential claw usually removed in first
few days of puppy's life

Dorsal. Top or back of dog's body

## E

Edema. Body tissues contain an excessive amount of
tissue   fluid

Effleurage. Stroking. Long flowing stroke

Etheric Double. Energy level closest to the physical
animal. Mirror image of physical

Extend, extension. Movement stretches and elongates
muscle –away from midline of body

## F

Fascia. Connective tissue

Fat. Adipose tissue of the body; serves as energy
reserve, inhibits heat loss, protects organs and
gives pleasing contours to body
Field Theory of Energy. Description of the body as an
energy field with many well-measured
components
Flex, Flexion. Movement shortens and bulges muscle
– toward midline of body
Fold of the flank. Webbing of skin in front of thigh.
Massage of this point has calming effect
Friction. Rapid movement of hands on body surface.
Creates heat, warming muscles and skin

**G**
Grounding. Brings energy and attention to the ground
~ to the source earth. Final strokes of massage

**H**
Hock. Rear ankle
Holding. Maintaining pressure on a point or position of
body part
Holding pattern. Unconscious way muscles are
held in given emotional or physical situations
Homeostasis. State of dynamic equilibrium maintained
by processes of feed-back and regulation
Integration shake. Partial or full body shake.
Demonstration and process of accepting and
owning changes to muscle and/or emotional
holding patterns
Integration stroke. Completion stroke to integrate or
"set" bodywork on therapy segment during
massage. Smoothing

**J**
Joints. Articulation. Functional junction between
bones. They bind the parts of the skeleton
together and enable body parts to move in
response to muscle contractions
Joint Capsule. Flexible tubular structures that hold
ends of the bones together
Joint movement. *Controlled* movement within the
normal range of motion

# K

Krebs cycle. Oxidization of pyruvic acid to liberate energy in cells. Carbohydrates and fats are used in production of energy

# L

Lactic acid. End product of anaerobic respiration, causing oxygen debt, muscle fatigue, accounts for burning sensation in muscles and next-day muscle aches

Ligament. Band or sheet of strong fibrous connective tissue connecting bones, cartilages and other structures and  serving as a support or for attachment of fascia or muscles

Limbic System Emotional brain of nervous system (Stomach Meridian)

Limbic System.  A group of interconnected deep brain structures, common to all mammals, and involved in olfaction, emotion, motivation, behavior, and various  autonomic functions

Lumbar. Lower back. The part of the body between the ribs and the hipbones.

Lymph Thin colorless fluid that carries white blood cells. Matrix for immune system

Lymph nodes

> Largest node is Spleen
> 5 Major Nodes [filtrate lymphatic fluid]
>> Submandibular, under the jaw
>> Prescapular, in front of shoulder blade
>> Axillary, front legs arm pit
>>> Inguinal, groin
>>> Popliteal, back of stifle, knee

# M

Meridian Circadian Rhythm times.

| Yin | | Yang | |
|---|---|---|---|
| Liver | 1-3 AM | Gall Bladder | 11-1 AM |
| Cardiac | 11-1 PM | Small Intestine | 1-3 PM |
| Pericardium | 7-9 PM | Triple Heater | 9-11 PM |
| Spleen | 9-11 AM | Stomach | 7-9 AM |
| Lung | 3-5 AM | Large Intestine | 5-7 |
| Kidney | 5-7 PM | Bladder | 3-5 PM |
| Conception v. Night | | Governing v. Day | |

| Yin | Yang |
|---|---|
| Conception v. -- CV | Governing v. -- GV |
| Liver -- L | Gall Bladder – GB |
| Cardiac -- C | Small Intestine – SI |
| Pericardium – P (ventral) | Triple Heater-- TH |
| Spleen – SP | Stomach -- ST |
| Lung -- LU | Large Intestine –LI |
| Kidney – K | Bladder -- BL |

Meridian system. Linear network of acupressure points that access internal body systems

Muscle memory. Muscle tissue held in fixed, protected position. Also, the memory held within the muscle cells. Holding pattern

Muscle testing/ Applied Kinesiology. Method of accessing body wisdom

**O**

Occipital protuberance. Raised area at back of scull on occipital bone

Opposition. Muscle that fixes or opposes movement of flexion or extension

**P**

Pads. Hard waterproof tissues on inferior sides of paws

Pain drain. Method in Healing Touch of drawing off imbalanced Ch'i

Palliative. To moderate the intensity of discomfort (at end of life), Ease pain without healing

Palpation. To assess with touch

Pastern. Area of hind leg just below the hock

Percussion. Tapping or patting

Perspiration. Release of heat through evaporation from tongue & pads of feet

PetMassage. Method of animal massage

Petrissage. Deep tissue stroking. Kneading.

Physiology. Functions and processes of parts of the body. What it does

**R**

Reactive Movement Massage. Massage in response to animal communication

Recoil. Movement of positional release in which body or energy pulls back into the body

Release. Softening of held muscle knot, breath, gas, imagery, memory and/or emotion – seen as "twitch" or yawn

Rescue Remedy. Bach Flower homeopathic flower essences

Respiration. Movement of air/ energy through nose, mouth, lungs

Ripple effect. Further unwinding of body and emotional holding patterns after massage sequence or session

Rocking. Large movement of body or body parts back and forth

Rolling. Compressed tissues moved in a to-and-fro motion; Fingers are extended and held together, pressure with the palms

ROE. Range of Emotion

Rom. Range of Motion

Ruffling. Stimulation of layers on aura/energy field

**S**

Sacrum. Semi-fused bones in vertebra at base of tail

Sagittal Crest. Ridge on skull from top of stop to occipital protuberance

Senses. Abilities that dogs use to cognate their world

Skeleton. Bony framework of body. Attachment sites of muscles

Skin rolling. Drawing skin up away from underlying structures and releasing

Smoothing. Long Effleurage stroke completes massage segment

Snag. Rough, sharp or jagged projecting part on skin, coat or energy level

Stifle. Knee

Stillness place. Quiet space within therapist and dog where healing begins and happens

Stroke. Touch with movement

Subcutaneous. Below the cutaneous, upper layer of
the skin
Subtle body. Aura

**T**

Tarsus. Ankle
Tendon. Inelastic cords of fibrous tissue at the ends of muscles
that connect them to bones
Thoracic. Thorax. Area of body within ribcage
Throatlatch. Base of throat
Ting Point. Located at the end or beginning of a
meridian, it is a transition point from one
meridian channel to the next. Provides
important information about the well being of
your dog
Touch, passive. Resting hand with *very* light (5 grams)
pressure. No lateral movement
Touch, pulsating. Vibration
Trigger point. Marble in the mud. Build up of lactic
acid. "Knot"
Triple heater. Meridians that regulate energy and
water metabolism, digestion, heat regulator

**U**
Unwinding. Movement as body releases tightness and
flows to          its place of comfort
Unruffling. Calming of layers on aura/energy field

**V**
Valley. Indentation between muscles, tendons,
ligaments, and bones   Acupressure sites. Above
the body they are felt as energy ripples
Ventral. Underside or bottom of dog's body
Vibration. Rapid back and forth lateral movement.
Gross (big) or subtle (tiny) movements

**W**
Web. Skin between toes, between knee and hip, fold
of the flank
Withers. High point above shoulders

# Y

Yang. Dynamic of hot, light, dry, upper, male
attributes of energy:

Yawn. Involuntary opening of mouth with intake of a
deep breath Release of $CO_2$, intake of $O_2$,
stretching movement that helps release tension
in the jaw and neck Yawning may stimulate
observers to yawn

Yin. Dynamic of attributes of energy: cool, dark, moist,
lower, female

Yin-Yang. Symbol of interrelatedness and dependence
of opposites

# Z

Zipper. Energetic opening that is accessed to open or
lock passage to etheric armoring

# Index

# Other fine PetMassage™ CDs, DVDs and books

## PetMassage™ Energy Work With Dogs
*Assessing The Magnificent Body Language & Body Wisdom of the Dog through Acupressure, Chakra Balancing & Positional Release*

Available as a book and audio CD set

The best ways to learn PetMassage™ Energy Work With Dogs are to read it, listen to it, and practice it.

Learn while driving around in your car!

PetMassage™ Energy Work with Dogs 5 Audio CD's 5 hours, with 52 minutes of instruction.

**PetMassage™ Energy Work 5-Audio CD set**
*$44.95+ $7.00 s/h*

# TRANSITIONS PetMassage Energy Work for the Aging & Dying

Dog celebrates life ... and death. This is a book of hope and love that will comfort you during the difficult times of impending loss.

TRANSITIONS teaches ways to be empowered during the last few months of your dog's life. It chronicles the story of the last days of Oskar the boxer, and the powerful last PetMassage™ session author, Jonathan Rudinger  shared with his cherished canine PetMassage™ teaching assistant.

This is a beautiful guide in the use of touch and intention for sharing a loving goodbye.

Jonathan Rudinger

**TRANSITIONS**

**PetMassage Energy Work for the Aging & Dying Dog**

PetMassage™ Training and Research Institute

Learn TRANSITIONS PetMassage™. TRANSITIONS PetMassage Energy Work for the Aging & Dying Dog is only $20.

Order yours at www.petmassage.com

# Dogs Kids PetMassage™

This is a delightful book that teaches kids the valuable skills of compassionate touch, sensitivity and awareness. In addition to basic hands-on canine massage this book covers principles of dog handling safety.

The therapeutic power of touch along with the enjoyment and value of PetMassage join with the natural connection children have with their dogs. Learning and practicing PetMassage™ is more than just petting dogs!

This is the perfect (educational) gift for every one of the children who loves dogs. Large format: 8 1/2 X 11, illustrated, suitable for all grade levels.

**Dogs Kids PetMassage™** is the core of the 3-part

PetMassage for Kids™ set which also includes the 60-**minute** PetMassage™ **A Kids Guide to Massaging Dogs**, DVD, and the PetMassage™ **Doggie Songs for Kids** CD.

**PetMassage for Kids™** is the educational material for the popular after school, home school, camp and scout programs.

The **Dogs Kids PetMassage** book by itself is only $16.95. All three are only $45. Order yours at www.petmassage.com